Prelude to a Private NHS

privatising public services by stealth

Elitham B Turya MSc FRCPCH MBA
healthcare professional and student of social policy

Edukom
www.edukom.co.uk

Prelude to a Private NHS

Edukom
5 Cambridge Close
Sale, Manchester
England M33 4YJ

www.edukom.co.uk
info@edukom.co.uk

First published by Edukom 2003

ISBN 0-9515819- 8- 8

Prelude to a Private NHS

Preface

Prelude to a private NHS grew from *Prelude to a private national health service*, a dissertation for the final lap of the Warwick MBA (self-sponsored distance learning), submitted in March 2001.

The dissertation examined *'evidence'* from published material that pointed to a tendency by governments to quietly transfer essential NHS services back into private hands– *privatising the NHS by stealth.*

While privatising the welfare state accelerates, there is hardly any debate in parliament of the shift in social policy. Do the Conservatives, the Liberal Democrats and Labour have a secret pact to privatise the NHS in England and Wales?

Scotland seems to have a different solution for NHS reforms. The *National Health Service Reforms (Scotland) Bill* might turn out better than the English equivalent. Why is the English departure from socialism not strongly opposed by the Labour left?

Prelude to a Private NHS collates publicly available information (in books, newspapers, TV and radio broadcasts and on the internet) to show that Labour has prepared the welfare state, and the NHS in particular, for privatisation– *to shed the electoral risk of funding welfare services from general taxation.*

'References' gives details of sources cited in the text and these will lead you to more detailed discussions.

Beware of *market forces, performance contracts* and *payment for results.* Shake (understand) the mantra before swallowing.

---

1. Introduction

Prelude to a Private NHS starts with a brief review of the social and healthcare history of Britain. It notes that the 1834 *Poor Law Amendment Act* consolidated care of the poor and formalised the principle of *economy and deterrence* and less eligibility and established workhouse, the 1848 *Public Health Act* which combated rampant infectious disease and squalor, the 1906 *Education (Provision of Meals) Act that* established a school medical service and the 1911 *National Insurance Act* that established the principle of direct state involvement in ensuring the welfare of its citizens. The work of Charles Booth and Joseph Rowntree in demonstrating the true causes of poverty and the impact of the labour movement in eroding the principle of *economy and deterrence* in the care of the poor are examined.

Failure of local authority and voluntary hospitals to a meet the health needs of the population is examined. The voluntary healthcare sector could not, and private healthcare providers would not adequately meet health needs of the poor.

The review of social history discusses the impact of the 2nd World War on social attitudes, and how the war effort facilitated the creation of the welfare state. The 1944 *Education Act* that established free primary, secondary and further education, the *Family Allowances Act* that introduced universal child allowance, the 1946 *National Insurance* and *National Industrial Injuries* Acts that guaranteed financial protection during maternity, sickness, unemployment, industrial injury, widowhood, and retirement– *"from the cradle to the grave,"* as well as the *1946 National Health Service Act* that established the NHS to tackle the scourge of *Disease* are noted.

In the hurry to reform/deform the NHS, Labour has forgotten its roots and the history of health care in Britain. Social history teaches that private and charitable hospitals were unable to provide adequate health care to the people. The *1946 National Health Service Act* was passed to provide better access to health care.

How will future voluntary and private health care providers avoid the *principle of economy and deterrence,* and *less eligibility*– reverting to something reminiscent of the Poor Law?

Electoral risk of welfare services

The Labour government is worried about the electoral risks of accelerating welfare costs– the impact of higher taxes on its future electability. The NHS, the most popular of welfare services, has about 1.25 million employees and a budget of about £68.7bn (2003 - 4). The British public love the NHS, but also abandon politicians who increase taxes.

If Labour significantly increased headline taxes (income tax and VAT), it could alienate converts from 'middle England'– the middle class. If the electorate were persuaded by Tories that this Labour government had set excessive taxes, the Labour party would lose the next general election.

Therefore the Labour government must raise revenue for public services without overt excessive tax increases. It appears that Labour agrees with the Tories on a major social policy– privatising health care without alienating the majority of the electorate.

Who needs the NHS?

The history of health and social policy before the 2nd World War shows that philosophical and economic beliefs created and sustained the Poor Law, but also contributed to the birth of the NHS.

The economic and philosophical arguments for 'free market forces' that gave birth to, and sustained the Poor Law are discussed. The labour movement and advocacy for a humane collective social action to remedy and prevent the suffering of the poor are reviewed. The origin of tensions between doctors and the Department of Health (DH) in successive governments is briefly discussed.

Commissioning (buying) of health care by GP collectives or primary care trusts (PCTs), from NHS and private health service providers, the private finance initiative, the 'concordat' with private medicine, the need for Diagnosis and Treatment Centres, and imminent foundation hospitals are examined for their relevance and social utility.

Do PCTs inhibit collaboration in the NHS?

The *1997 NHS Primary Care Act* created barriers to communication between PCT and hospital trusts. The need for, and the bureaucracy of consulting several PCTs, private health providers, charitable organisation and other stakeholders works as if it was designed to destroy NHS collaboration, is summarised.

Why hide NHS privatisations?

It is difficult to understand why major utilities (electricity, water, gas, telecommunications and council housing) were publicly privatised but Conservative and Labour governments stealthily transfer NHS services (ophthalmic, dentistry, care of the elderly, infrastructure, and elective surgery) to private providers. Are they afraid of being voted out office should the public prematurely believe that *the NHS is to be privatised*?

Finding new money without raising taxes

The Labour government, ever afraid of overtly raising headline taxes, continues to find *'new money'* to fund public services until they are ready for privatisation. While preparing the NHS for privatisation, the government:

- raises revenue through patient charges and restrains demand through implicit rationing

- uses the private finance initiative (PFI) to hide capital expenditure from headline news (creative accounting)

- deliberately shifts blame for the ills of the NHS from government policy to NHS staff

- introduces unworkable reforms to destabilise the NHS and convince the public of the need for privatising health care

- ensures that the public is not provoked into electoral revolt by disguising destabilisation of public sector services as *'enhancing choice.'*

Despite (or because of) a new managerialism, capital charges and efficiency savings and purchaser/provider splits, waiting lists and budget overspends continue to grow.

For a long time governments did not accept that the main cause of financial problems in the NHS was deliberate under-funding and unstable corporate leadership. Although extra money has been found, it is doubtful if it will reverse the damage caused by 50 years of under-funding and neglect and achieve north European standards soon.

Is Labour implementing a privatisation agenda?

Is Labour implementing the 1987 Conservative Agenda for privatising the NHS? Is Labour unwittingly preparing the NHS for Conservatives to privatise when they return to government?

Even if it is laudable that Labour has no plans to privatise the NHS, the Tories will appreciate Labour's efforts in getting the NHS ready for privatisation. The Tories and Liberal Democrats have not opposed Labour NHS reforms. They have criticised Labour for being too timid!

PFI converts public serves into private property

Using PFI to finance NHS developments and obliging future taxpayers to honour 9 -15% interest rates on 25 - 50 years mortgages is an excellent vehicle for transferring public property to the private sector.

Closing hospital beds to create 'need for capacity'

DTCs– elective surgery wards would be a simpler and more accurate description, but of limited use for electioneering purposes– are '*growing capacity*' or rather replacing capacity decimated by Tory *efficiency drives* and Labour's compulsory PFI financing. DTCs provide elective surgery for NHS patients. The surgery is performed in units built by the NHS, but managed by the private sector. While the NHS pays private surgeons to operate on NHS patients, NHS surgeons may be idle in hospitals whose capacity was decimated by 'efficiency savings or PFI funding.

Hospitals are short of capacity (beds) because:

- beds were closed by Tory efficiency savings, and/or
- less capacity (smaller hospitals) was 'delivered' under PFI.

NHS surgical teams cancel elective surgery because surgical beds are filled by emergency admissions. This 100% bed occupancy is what Tory and Labour efficiency drives and Labour's PFI planned and achieved! Now Diagnosis and Treatment Centres must 're-grow capacity' for the private sector to exploit.

- Why won't Labour *'grow capacity'* in every hospital where elective surgery is often cancelled because surgical beds are occupied by emergencies?

- Have future electioneering needs encouraged the government to create, deliver and publicise *identifiable* projects (DTCs), to improve *patient choice* for elective surgery, and chances of a grateful electorate voting Labour?

Accelerating measures to destabilise the NHS

Destabilisation of the NHS is underway through obligatory PFIs, commissioning health care, the *'concordat with the private and voluntary health care provider sector'*, diagnosis and treatment centres and the spectre of foundation hospitals'.

Insuring against electoral revolt

Labour spin-doctors have ensured that the public do not realise that their beloved NHS is being privatised by the back door. Labour sells PFI, concordat with private medicine and diagnosis and treatment centres as improving patient choice. The press has been most helpful by continually highlighting 'health care scandals' and asserting that the nation's health would be better without the NHS.

Who will save the welfare state?

Even if the electorate objected to Labour's stewardship of public services, no other major political party is eager to save the NHS. The Liberal Democrats admire Labour's social policy; the Conservatives would love the opportunity to dismantle the welfare state.

Salvation for the NHS could emerge from the aftermath of failures of the concordat with private medicine, major PFI projects and the medical insurance market. It is unlikely that these systems would fail simultaneously– but it is possible.

Would a major political party be persuaded to maintain a health service funded through general taxation? Unlikely!

If established parties were unable or unwilling to maintain a national health service, perhaps a new political party could emerge, like Labour did early in the 20th century, to champion the cause the working class, a role abandoned by the Liberal Party.

The new party could champion those who could neither get medical insurance, afford education for their children, nor private housing.

---

2. Health care before 2nd World War

2.1 Determinants of social care before 1939

In the 100 years before the British National Health Service was formed, the battle against disease was fought on several overlapping fronts. Sanitation, hygiene and other preventive measures were enforced by legislation enacted after cholera and typhoid epidemics. Surgical disinfectants and antisepsis led to reduction in maternal mortality and better infant survival. Medical treatment became more prominent with advances in science and the arrival of effective drugs.

The overlapping fronts in the battle against disease were:

- the 1834 *Poor Law Amendment Act* consolidated care of the poor but also affirmed that public expenditure should be severely restricted and if possible, reduced

- the public health movement and the 1848 *Public Health Act* ensured adequate and safe water supplies, drainage and sewage disposal

- the 1906 *Education (Provision of Meals) Act* established a school medical service. It was prompted by the appalling physical condition of volunteers for the Boer War, who, like most of the population, were malnourished and unfit

- under the 1911 *National Insurance Act* the state contracted with doctors (GPs) to provide medical care for low income workers (those earning less than £160 per year)

- the 1929 *Local Government Act* transferred responsibility for the poor, workhouses and infirmaries to local authority health departments.

2.2 The public health movement

The 1848 *Public Health Act* was passed to combat rampant infectious disease and squalor. It ensured adequate water supplies, drainage and sewerage disposal in response to cholera and typhoid outbreaks.

A 'General Board of Health' was established to control the sanitary work of local authorities. Subsequent decline in infectious diseases was due to preventive public health measures following the *Public Health Act* rather curative medicine– there were few effective drugs.

A series of *Public Health Acts* created supervisory and regulatory functions for public health services. They established a medical officer of health (MOH), a sanitary inspector and a housing surveyor as key workers in local authority health service (Leathard 1990).

The MOH also organised immunisation against infectious diseases. In 1789 Edward Jenner had published a seminal paper on preventing smallpox by inoculation with cowpox. Free childhood vaccination began in 1840 (Ham 1999).

Demonstrating that improved sanitation leads to better health was the most important lesson. By the end of the nineteenth century the state, through local authorities, had taken over responsibilities for public health– protecting the community rather than aiding sick individuals.

2.3 An unhealthy population

Many volunteers for the Boer War in South Africa (1899-1901) were malnourished, short, crippled by rickets, and unfit. A government '*Committee on Physical Deterioration*' of the population reported in 1904 confirming the poor physical condition of population– young and old.

The Liberal party won the1906 general election and introduced several social reforms. The *1906 Education (Provision of Meals) Act* established a school medical service in 1907. Old age pensions started in 1908 (Leathard 1990).

2.4 National Insurance and medical care

Through the 1911 *National Insurance Act,* the state contracted with GPs to provide curative medical care for workers earning less than £160 per year. National insurance contributions were paid by the worker, the employer, and for the first time, by the state. In sickness and unemployment, an income was paid to insured workers from the fund (Cartwright 1977).

Liberal Prime Minister, Lloyd George, got the *National Insurance Act* passed against opposition from those who believed that public expenditure on the care of paupers should be restricted and, if possible reduced. The medical profession too, fearful of the effect of state control on their work and incomes, opposed the legislation (Cartwright 1977).

Doctors accepted the scheme when the government agreed that payment would be based on a capitation system– the number of patients on a doctor's list, rather than on a salary. This preserved the GP's independence, a status which they fight to retain today.

Before the *National Insurance Act,* health care was episodic, haphazard and depended on a patient's ability to pay. The rich paid for the services of eminent or fashionable doctors. Such doctors' income came from a carefully nurtured private practice.

The poor received medical care under the *1834 Poor Law Amendment Act* which followed the principle of *economy and deterrence*– that in caring for paupers, public expenditure should be restricted and, if possible reduced. This belief had to be overcome before politicians could campaign for, and government could take steps to reduce poverty and disease.

Public health and personal curative care were deliberately kept apart under the Poor Law. The destitute sick could be seen at home by council medical officers. But services were usually inadequate or late. The destitute sick could also present themselves at hospitals, charity clinics and public dispensaries for treatment without referral from any doctor.

Except for the rich and the poor, most people were treated by GPs for a fee. Although they could charge what they wished many GPs had difficulty in collecting their fees in poor areas. Poverty forced many families to choose between buying food and getting treatment for the sick. Priority for treatment was given to the wage earner and children, then the mother, with the elderly coming last.

The national insurance scheme covered only the insured manual worker and not his family. It did not include the self-employed, the unemployed, non-manual workers like clerks, nurses and teachers and members of the middle class. It was designed for employed members of the working class only.

The scheme did not pay for hospital and specialist care. Some insurers did not provide dental care or spectacles. Nevertheless the 1911 *National Insurance Act* was a major advance in social policy. The state accepted its role in providing health care of its people (Leathard 1990).

2.5 Hospital services

The Poor Law dictated how medical care for the poor was organised. Most sick poor people received medical care in workhouses where 'nursing' was done by other inmates (Leathard 1990).

The principle of *economy and deterrence* (*less eligibility*) led to the creation of workhouses so bad that the destitute and sick were afraid to seek relief therein (Cartwright 1977).

Hospitals were built mainly to protect the community from the spread of infection, but also to care for the destitute sick.

Gradually a number of purpose-built infirmaries with salaried medical staff and trained nurses were built. Such hospitals gradually ceased to be regarded as part of the Poor Law service (Cartwright 1977, Leathard 1990).

By 1914, at the start of the 1st World War, local authorities were responsible for public health, infectious disease hospitals, the destitute sick and long-term care. The 1929 *Local Government Act* transferred responsibility for workhouses and infirmaries to local authorities. Qualified health professionals were employed and the standard of care improved.

Although municipal hospitals were open to everyone, rich or poor, the *Local Government Act* did not remove the aura of the Poor Law. Local authorities charged a fee for hospital services according to the individual's ability to pay. Nevertheless it was possible for the poor to get free treatment or to pay nominal fee. High income groups avoided municipal hospitals.

Hospital services developed along two uncoordinated lines– municipal and voluntary– each catering for different sections of the community. By 1939 there were about 1750 local authority hospitals of all types.

Voluntary hospitals served higher income groups, were the mainstay of specialist care, and medical education and training (Webster 1995).

2.6 Funding crises in voluntary hospitals

Voluntary hospitals formed the core of specialist hospital services before the NHS. They trained all doctors and most nurses. Local authority hospitals were neither able nor willing to extend their resources into the training of health workers (Leathard 1990). The rich and well off were drawn by the superior facilities of voluntary hospitals.

Although not obliged by law to treat poor patients, excluding them ran against the spirit of voluntarism. Specialist treatment for the poor was financed by charging richer patients higher fees– an enforced medical charity.

Voluntary hospitals were run on endowments, voluntary donations, patient payments, insurance funds, and volunteer workers. Famous medical teaching centres attracted unpaid specialists and consultants.

Trade unions built hospitals for their members. Local GPs built ant ran cottage hospitals.

Voluntary hospital finances were strained most of the time. A committee led by Viscount Cave recommended in 1921, that government should donate £1,000,000 to assist hospitals at risk of bankruptcy. Only £500,000 was donated, and government would not accept responsibility for meeting the deficit.

In 1889, the House of Lords set up a committee to enquire into the financial viability of London voluntary hospitals. The Lords' committee recommended in 1891 that all London hospitals should be placed under the control of an independent central board. The report warned that, unless urgent action was taken, all voluntary hospitals would need government support. Nothing was done (Leathard 1990).

In 1896, the Prince of Wales invited leading industrialists, doctors, financiers and Church dignitaries to discuss the financial crisis facing London's voluntary hospitals. The meeting led to the formation of the Prince of Wales' Hospital Fund for London. The Fund found that most of the financial crises were caused by poor accounting practices. No hospital was thereafter given financial help unless it adopted standard accounting methods.

The Prince's Fund persuaded some small hospitals to amalgamate into more economically viable units. By the end of 1902 the Fund had raised over £800,000 and by 1910 it provided about 10% of the total running cost of London voluntary hospitals.

The Prince's Fund (later the 'King's Fund') fulfilled the functions of a central board. However, it was neither powerful enough, nor did it have adequate resources to ensure efficient hospital services.

Nevertheless without the King's Fund, London voluntary hospitals would have become bankrupt and closed sooner (Cartwright 1977, Leathard 1990).

Despite the King's Fund, the financial situation got so bad that in April 1920, the chairman of the London Hospital told the government that voluntary hospitals would close unless the government provided one-third of their income. Later that year a number of voluntary hospitals closed beds. Government provided £700,000 and the King's Fund added another £250,000– the crisis was averted. However, a bill that could have solved the hospitals' funding problems, integrated curative and preventive medicine was defeated in the Lords (Cartwright 1977).

By 1944 there were about 1000 voluntary hospitals of different size, age, function, and national distribution (Leathard 1990).

2.7 Shortcomings of health care before 1939

By 1939 public health measures had eliminated cholera, typhoid and smallpox epidemics. Maternal and infant mortality rates had declined by 70% from those of 1901; male average life expectancy at birth had risen from 45 to 60 years.

Despite these gains there were major deficiencies:

- health services, hospitals, specialists and general practitioners, were badly distributed with poorer areas sparsely served

- there was marked adequacies in social and health service because of lack of resources and trained workers (Cartwright 1977)

- hospital waiting lists were long because of bed shortages and lack of trained personnel (Leathard 1990)

- the 1911 *National Insurance Act* covered less than half of the population. It excluded children, wives, the unemployed and self-employed, higher income employees and old people.

- voluntary hospitals were short of money most of the time and frequently threatened with bankruptcy. Many went bankrupt and closed.

---

3. Origins of the NHS

Health care in Britain has developed by evolution rather than revolution. The emergence of a national health service was shaped by a shift from a paternalistic 'laissez-faire' market philosophy to a society supportive of collective action to minimise suffering and poverty (Ham 1999).

3.1 The influence of humanist philosophies

For about a 100 years before 1945, a number of philosophers argued that it was desirable to promote the greatest happiness for the greatest number of people– the principle of utility. John S Mill in 1861 advocated, in *Utilitarianism*, radical reforms in education, political justice and health care (JS Mill, et al 1987). His essay popularised the concept of the 'common good'.

While rationalist philosophers and evangelical Christians supported collective action to eliminate human suffering, the Tories strongly opposed such actions (Leathard 1990). They affirmed their belief that poverty was the individual's fault, and that government action could not change the position of the poor, and that only the market could efficiently distribute goods and services to the benefit of society (Smith 1982).

Surveys by Joseph Rowntree (www.jrrt.org.uk) in York in 1901 and Charles Booth (http://lse.ac.uk) in London in 1903 of people's living conditions revealed shocking poverty, misery and disease among the poor. Rowntree and Booth showed that the most important causes of poverty were low wages and interrupted earnings from sickness, unemployment, and old age. It was no longer credible to claim that the poor were responsible for their poverty.

3.2 Impact of the labour movement

The desire for collective action in social welfare was assisted by the growing strength of the labour movement, the extension of the right to vote in 1867, the emergence of Labour MPs in 1906, the influence of the reformist Fabians Society and the rise of socialism. British socialism called for collective action to overcome the inefficiency and injustice of a capitalist market economy (Leathard, 1990).

Despite Tory belief in free market economics, government expenditure on health services in England and Wales increased from £5.6m in 1900 to £51m in 1914 (Webster 1995).

Although essential and welcome, economic growth, without a measure of wealth redistribution, was seen as no solution to social problems. Charity could only touch the margins of need and deprivation. Increasingly it was felt that the only effective solution was for the state to address social and economic hardships and to prevent them (Leathard, 1990).

3.3 Financial failure of voluntary hospitals

Impending bankruptcy of London voluntary hospitals gave impetus to searches for a more stable system for funding health care (Cartwright 1977, Leathard 1990).

3.4 Social levelling by 2nd World War

Between 1939 and 1945, there was a transient but effective co-ordination of health services for the war effort. Many war veterans and civilians believed the country should not return to the chaos that existed in health and social care before the war (Leathard, 1990).

The war effort forced all social classes into co-operative activity. Arrangements to meet social needs, such as emergency health care, food distribution, transfer of children from cities to the safer countryside and fighting on the battlefield, broke social barriers and brought people to a more equal level. Social biases and behavioural patterns were transformed by the war effort.

The decline in social barriers enabled post war political activism in favour of egalitarian social policies to be heard sympathetically. In the climate of austerity, sharing resources and risks, radical social changes became more acceptable (Leathard, 1990).

3.5 Arrival of the Welfare State

In August 1945 the Labour Party won the general election with an overwhelming majority. The Labour government passed legislation that nationalised and rationalised major public services and altered the social policy landscape. Social welfare measures would be financed from general taxation.

The 1944 *Education Act* established free universal education for all children at primary, secondary higher levels, while the *Family Allowances Act* introduced a universal system of payments (child allowance) for each child up to leaving school.

The Beveridge Report (1942) on *Social Insurance and Allied Services* led to the 1946 *National Insurance Act* and the *National Industrial Injuries Act.* These Acts guaranteed every working person would be protected. Married women secured entitlement through their husband's contributions. Entitlements would cover loss of earnings during maternity, unemployment, sickness, industrial injury, widowhood, and retirement– from the cradle to the grave.

Other legislation introduced housing subsidies and required local authorities to build houses to let. Council housing was no longer confined to the 'working class' but extended to all in need of housing. By enacting measures for comprehensive social services, the state accepted responsibility for the welfare of its citizens. It moved away from the stigma of the Poor Law and principle of *economy and deterrence*.

However, the 1946 *National Insurance Act* contained an alternative model for funding social security in which the individual, the state and or employer insure against loss of earnings through compulsory contributions. That model has been extended by *National Insurance Contributions Act 2002* to raising funds for a national health service.

3.6 Birth of a national health service

The aim of the 1942 Beveridge Report was to aid post-war reconstruction by combating the *'five giants'* of *"Disease, Ignorance, Squalor, Idleness* and *Want"* by legislation. The *1946 National Health Service Act* was passed to tackle the *'Disease'* giant (Timmins 1996). The NHS was designed to offer an integrated, effective, efficient, comprehensive, universally accessible service to the people. Financed from taxation, it was to be free of charge at the point of use. The NHS was established to improve the distribution, increase the volume and quality of services.

GPs could accept or refuse patients, and patients could change doctors as they wished. Private practice was permitted so that neither patients nor doctors were compelled to join the NHS.

3.7 Structure of a national health service

The head of the NHS would be the Minister of Health. The NHS would include mental health, as well as physical health services. The Minister would delegate general administration to regional and local bodies based on university teaching hospitals. Regional bodies would employ people with local experience and knowledge (Webster 1991).

Hospital and Specialist Services

Local authority, voluntary and university hospitals were nationalised. Teaching hospitals were given a special status. Regional hospital boards would include representatives from local authorities, people nominated by the Minister, the local university and representatives of local doctors. University hospitals would provide undergraduate and post-graduate teaching. They were also permitted to carry out research.

Consultants could be either full time or part-time employees, with their salary based on the number of hours worked in the NHS. Part-time consultants were allowed private practice outside their contracted hours. They could admit fee-paying patients into NHS hospital beds. The Minister of health, Aneurin Bevan, stated that:

"... unless we permit some fee-paying patients in public hospitals, there will be a rash of nursing homes all over the country." (Cartwright 1977).

Local authority services

Local authorities would be responsible for providing and maintaining health and dental centres. They would also be responsible for school medical services, maternity and child welfare (in association with hospitals), domiciliary midwifery, vaccination and immunisation, health visiting, home nursing, home help in time of sickness, care for the sick and convalescents, ambulance and mental health services.

General practitioner and dental services

The NHS would provide a comprehensive general medical service delivered by general medical practitioners. The service would include medicines, drugs and appliances for the whole population from 5th July 1948. There would be separate Local Executive Committees for general medical and dental services.

GPs and dentists retained their 'independent contractor' status, their practices and received a salary as well as capitation fees. Restrictions were imposed on opening new practices in 'popular' areas (Cartwright, 1977). Dentists' salary and fees scales would be set by a national body (Webster 1991); extra payments would be based on claims after dental treatment.

General practice and dental services could be provided from private premises if there was no room in local authority premises. Most dental services are run from private premises.

3.8 Doctors' reaction to the new service

In 1945, Clement Attlee, Labour Prime Minister, entrusted the Ministry of Health to Aneurin Bevan. The appointment of a politician from the left wing of the party as Minister of Health terrified the conservative British Medical Association (BMA). The appointment of a minister from the more socialist wing of the Labour party may have contributed to the mistrust surrounding negotiations of terms under which doctors' would work in the new service.

The BMA feared that the government was motivated by a hidden agenda and so it adopted a defensive posture while working out the true motives of the reforms (Webster 1998).

The medical profession mildly welcomed the *National Health Service Act.* As doctors were essential to the scheme, government negotiated with the BMA, a doctors trade union, terms for working under the Act. The BMA was experienced in dealing with governments and secured better terms for doctors than other cadres received (Cartwright 1977).

The BMA obtained better terms for doctors because it had the skill and influence to negotiate them. This simple fact is often lost in discussions of the concessions government made to doctors at the start of the NHS. Other cadres did not have the organisation and skill to negotiate similar terms.

Doctors came from the upper and middle classes of society and had friends in powerful positions. Nurses and other cadres came from the working class, had few powerful friends, were not organised and therefore were relatively powerless (Cartwright 1977).

3.9 Popularity of the new health service

The NHS started relatively smoothly. Shortly after its launch, 97% of the population had registered with NHS doctors; 98% of GPs, 94% of dentists, and most pharmacists had joined the service (Leathard 1990).

---

4. Financing health care

4.1 Sources of NHS funding

The NHS is funded from consolidated funds (general tax), national insurance contributions, patient charges and capital refunds– a 6% charge on capital assets (Box 4.1)

Box 4.1: Sources of financing (selected financial years)

Source of funds	**1988-89**	**1991-92**	**1993-94**	**1996-97**	**1998-99**
Total funding (£m)	**19317**	**26954**	**31275**	**36330**	**42131**
Consolidated fund	80.1%	94.7%	94.7%	93.7%	89.5%
National insurance	15.1%	14.0%	12.7%	12.2%	12.8%
Patient charges	3.1%	4.1%	3.1%	2.1%	2.1%
Capital refunds*	-	-	1.2%	3.0%	7.1%
Trust, debts, etc	1.7%	1.1%	1.1%	1.2%	1.3%

** identified separately from 1993-4, DH 2000*

Capital charges are supposed to remind the NHS of costs it would pay if its estates were rented from the private sector, and to improve efficiency in the deployment of financial resources (Shaoul, 1998).

4.2 Labour promises more money

Following concerns that the NHS was under-funded (Harrison et al 1997, Economist 1997) the Labour government promised to increase funding over several years (Klein and Dixon, 2000) because:

- demand for healthcare had increased by 50% (1990- 1996) and waiting lists for hospital services were longer

- higher patient expectations mean that patients are unwilling to quietly wait for treatment (Economist, 1997)

- developments in medical technological have increased options for, and the cost of treatment (Box 4.2)– more can be done for more people and it costs more money

- increase in the numbers of elderly people, most of whom have chronic conditions, means that the cost for treating conditions like hypertension, diabetes, arthritis and stroke is rising

- many health facilities are old and need rebuilding, upgrading and refurbishing.

Box 4.2: NHS expenditure per person

Year	Total NHS cost £ m	Total NHS cost per person £	Total NHS medicines cost £ m	NHS medicines/ person £	Medicines as a % of total cost
1980	11,257	200	826	37.86	8.9
1985	17,154	303	1,627	47.77	9.8
1990	28,246	448	2,533	60.75	8.9
1995	41,853	680	4,583	91.34	11.0
2000	57,067	878	7,073	120.63	12.4
2001	62,892	955	7,753	129.25	12.3

From ABPI (Association of the British Pharmaceutical Industry), 2002

However critical observers say that the additional £19.4 billion over four years is not enough to correct the legacy of 50 years of structural neglect and under-funding.

4.3 Where will the money come from?

The Labour government pledged in 2000, to raise UK spending on healthcare to north European average by 2006. This amounts to 9% of 1997 UK GDP. Spending on healthcare would have to increase by 9.7% a year (in real terms) over the next five years (£29.2bn) to reach the north European average of 9% (Appley and Boyle 2000).

Such levels of healthcare expenditure (Box 4.3) could be reached if government spent more on health care at a cost to other services, or by facilitating a large increase in healthcare spending from private healthcare providers.

Box 4.3: What wealthy countries spend on health care

Country	% GDP	% from public funds	% from private insurance
USA	13.7	44.2	33.2
Germany	10.5	75.3	6.9
France	9.6	76.4	12.2
Canada	9.5	69.6	1.9
Netherlands	8.6	70.4	17.7
Japan	7.6	78.3	n/a
UK	7.0	84.2	3.5

After Mathiason 2000

Private sector would not increase spending by 300%

The private sector would have to increase spending on healthcare by an unrealistic 300% to boost national spending on health care to 9%. How would the private health sector fund such an expansion of business? Would it be profitable? No– so they will not do it.

Massive privatisation of health services would also be inequitable. The poor and the uninsured would receive no care. However critics of the NHS say the time has come to abandon general taxation as the preferred method of financing health care. They cite alternative methods of funding, but rarely offer critical analysis of those methods in terms of efficiency and equity.

4.4 Options for funding health care

Health care can be financed by one, or a combination of methods– *social insurance, private health insurance, charging for healthcare or general taxation* (The NHS plan, DH 2000).

Let us briefly examine these options against the criteria of *efficiency* and *equity*– the rational basis for providing a public service in a compassionate and democratic country (Challis and Henwood 1994, Bevan 1998).

Efficiency– the ability of a proposal to achieve its intended objective, and to provide the greatest health gain with available resources (WHO 2000).

Equity– the extent to which a proposed charge matches an individual's ability to pay and provides a service to meet the individual's needs (Whitehead 1994).

4.4.1 Social insurance

Government could move wholesale to the French or German method of funding healthcare. In France funds are raised mainly from employees and employers and not the whole population.

In 2003, the Health Policy Consensus Group, a unit of the Institute for the Study of Civil Society, recommended that the NHS should be split into independent foundation hospitals funded from compulsory social insurance. Reasons given for changing from general taxation to social insurance were the same as those the NHS Plan gave for keeping general taxation as fairer and more equitable (DH 2000).

North European social insurance systems usually only involve payments by employees and employers. Only a segment of the population contributes to the fund and thus raises less money than could be raised through general taxation.

National health insurance contributions

An element of social insurance (national health insurance contributions) has operated in the UK since the 1946 *National Insurance Act.*

In 2002, parliament passed the National Insurance Contributions Act 2002, "*...to make provision for.... increasing national insurance contributions and for applying the increases towards the cost of the national health service"* (www.hmso.gov.uk/acts)

Personal income can now be taxed to fund health care. It is an income tax under another name.

Financing via social insurance may be inefficient

Continental European social insurance models are less efficient in several respects. While payers act as financial intermediaries between the healthcare system and the insurers, they do not scrutinise the efficiency and effectiveness of the system itself (DH 2000).

Despite, or because of, better patient choice, the French system is reported to be wasteful. More drugs are prescribed than in the NHS. France is learning from the NHS how to limit drug budgets (Henley 2000, OECD 2000).

Social insurance does not guarantee unlimited resources for healthcare. By limiting contribution rates or expenditure, the German and French governments determine overall expenditure under social insurance rather than insurers.

Financing via social insurance may be inequitable

The equity of social insurance in financing national health care depends on criteria for levying payments. A system that depends only on registered employees and employers is unfair to employees and employers.

The *National Insurance Contributions Act 2002* applies equally to the employed and self-employed. An extra 1% charge was imposed on earnings as low as £4,615 per year (£80.1 per week). There is no upper limit, so the well off pay more than if the 1% was on income tax.

4.4.2 Private health insurance

Boosting national health spending by encouraging private medical insurance requires tax incentives for individuals and/or employers to take out private medical insurance. In the presence of a publicly funded heath services, incentives may not work.

Why should an individual, with guaranteed access to free health care, pay for private health insurance? As long as there is a free and reasonably efficient NHS, medical insurance premiums are likely to remain unattractive (Hall 1999)

Funding via private insurance is inefficient

In 1990, the Tory government introduced tax relief on private medical insurance for people aged over 60 years. Despite the incentive, subscription to private medical insurance only rose by 1.6 % in seven years (Hall et al 1999).

Australia spent £1 billion in three years on tax incentives for private health insurance. The subsidies only halted the decline in policy-holders; and were taken up mainly by those who already had private medical insurance. The incentives increased public spending without boosting private spending on health care (Hall et al. 1999).

Using public money to fund tax incentives for private medical insurance diverts money from public services. It does not increase total health care expenditure (Emmerson, et al. 2000).

Funding via private insurance is expensive

Fragmented health care commissioning would lead to higher costs. Drug prices are, on average, 75% higher in the USA where health care is based on private medical insurance than in Britain's NHS. Attempts to control drug prices in USA have been condemned by economists and medical insurers as stifling the free market.

Administrative costs would rise significantly because of a fragmented bureaucracy in assessing risk, setting premiums, reviewing claims and making payment. Administrative costs are said to be 15% higher in the USA than in Canada mainly because of the cost of administering policies and claims.

Funding via private insurance is inequitable

Subsidising private health insurance would use public funds to expand private healthcare. Many people would not afford insurance premiums and so would have no access to health care (Rosenthal 1994).

"Private medical insurance shifts the burden of paying for health care from the healthy, young and wealthy to the unhealthy, old and poor. The cost of private health insurance rises the older and sicker the person - indeed beyond a certain age, and with chronic conditions, it is virtually impossible to get private insurance cover" (The NHS Plan, DH 2000).

4.4.3 Charging for healthcare

Advocates of charging for health care recommend higher charges to encourage responsible use of resources (*prevent some people using the service*) and to raise revenue.

Charging makes health care inefficient

When charges are high they generally reduce access and use of essential services (Willman 1998, WHO 2000). Less and delayed access may divert users from preventive to curative care. The diversion can, over time, result in higher healthcare costs without the population being healthier (DH 2000).

Low charges raises less revenue without reducing administrative costs, and does not raise user rates high enough for preventive care to become effective (Stocks 1993).

Charging may be inequitable

New charges increase health costs for the unhealthy, the old and the poor compared with the healthy, young or the rich. High charges reduce access by the poor (WHO 2000).

Prescription charges reduce drug utilisation by the non-exempt without affecting utilisation by the exempt. While charges reduce expenditure on prescribed drugs, 66% of the savings came from reduced use of services and not from increased revenue (Ryan and Birch 1991).

Discouraging people from using the NHS is reminiscent of the principle of *economy and deterrence* which was popular among 19th and early 20th century Tory politicians and economists, and created workhouses. It was assumed that the birth of the NHS would end *less eligibility* and *deterrence* in access to health care (Leathard 1990).

4.4.4 General taxation

General taxation (income, national health insurance, capital gains, corporate, import duties, stamp duty on house purchases, private insurance, etc.) funds public services like education, the army, the police, fire and rescue service, the judiciary as well as health care and traditional social work. It is claimed general taxation, is a fair and equitable method of insuring against sickness (NHS Plan, DH 2000).

Set higher taxes and risk losing political office

Increasing taxes (10p on income tax or increasing VAT to 27%) would raise enough revenue to reach north European average expenditure on health care. However, increasing total tax burden from 39.7% to over 56% would be politically risky (Appley and Boyle 2000). If Labour increased total taxation to 56%, it would lose the next general election.

---

5. NHS corporate dilemmas

5.1 Missing corporate radar

Unlike the BBC, which is governed by a royal charter, the NHS depends on the Department of Health (DH) for corporate policy, business strategy and corporate governance (Hutton 2000).

5.1.1 Cacophony of advice

Because the NHS lacks a defined corporate mission (charter, radar), many organisations (Box 5.1) compete to influence NHS policy.

Box 5.1: Example of offices/organisations vying for influence in health issues	
? CPPIH*	BAMM**
General Medical Council	British Medical Association
NHS Alliance	British Pharmaceutical Federation
NHS Confederation	Royal College of Midwives
Nurses and Midwives Council	Royal College of Nursing
Patient and public Involvement	Royal medical colleges (13+)
Patients' Association	Pharmaceutical Society
etc	**etc**

**CPPIH = Commission for Patient and Public Involvement in Healthcare*

***BAMM = British Association of Medical Managers*

Often it is difficult to determine which report or recommendations on a health issue will be read, let alone implemented. Sometimes royal colleges, confederations and trade unions speak as if they had the final say. In recent negotiations of a service contract for NHS consultants, it was often difficult to judge who was top dog– the secretary of state, the NHS Confederation or the DH directorate of human resources.

5.1.2 Minimal operational guidance

Often guidance on important operational issues is late, sketchy or incomplete. Recent reforms have been launched with minimal guidance. Primary care trusts were introduced with so little guidance that some health districts are still working out how to implement them, let alone manage locality commissioning of health services.

Hospital trusts are queuing to become 'foundation hospitals' before legal, financial and operational frameworks have been published let alone enacted by parliament (House of Commons (HOC) Health Select Committee 2003).

Areas of strategic confusion

The following are examples of NHS strategic confusion:

- Missing corporate leadership
- Undefined core activities
- Patient advocacy and markets
- The shrinking health service
- Shortage of native nurses
- Origin of specialist professionals.

5.2 Dos the NHS have defined core activities?

What elements of health care should be publicly funded? What must be offered by the NHS and what should be excluded?

Polls show that the public places high priority on treating children with life threatening conditions and on pain relief in terminally ill people. The lowest priority is given to infertility treatments and people over 75 years of age (Bowling 1996).

Failure to define core activities created a number of contradictions in local health authority policies. For example, while contraception was provided by most health authorities, the treatment of infertility was not? This implied that unwanted pregnancy was a disease to be prevented and infertility a lifestyle issue not deserving NHS funding– a painful anomaly for infertile couples (New 2000). Locality commissioning has not changed such anomalies.

The 1946 *National Health Service Act* did not define what the NHS should or should not provide. The scope for health care has grown with advances in diagnostics and therapeutics. Advances were incorporated into routine care without debate as to whether they should or should not be included. Drugs for impotence and male baldness competed with the treatment of cancer, hypertension, diabetes, maternity services and vaccines for childhood diseases.

Under New Labour's NHS reforms and waiting list crises, minor surgery is given priority in the scramble to meet numerical targets at the cost of complicated lengthy procedures (Timmins 2003).

5.2.1 Burden of disease did not decline

When the NHS was launched (5 July 1948), government believed that the cost of health care would decline as soon as the burden of disease was reduced. This was misguided. The true burden of disease was not known. No surveys were done before the NHS was established. With free health care, more people than expected came for treatment. Demand soon exceeded resources (Timmins 1996). In 1951, when the NHS was 2 years old, charging for dentures and spectacles was imposed to discourage demand and to raise revenue (Webster 1991).

5.2.2 Is medical progress too rapid for the Treasury?

Scientific progress has led to more diagnostic and treatment tools than were available in 1948. Medical discoveries are welcome by doctors and patients but they cost money. Perhaps the Treasury would be happier if no more discoveries were made. The need to fund them would not arise and there wound be less concern over the NHS bill, need for higher taxation and the risk of losing general elections.

5.2.3 Longer life, disability and disease

In 1998, average life expectancy in the UK was 74.9 years for men and 79.8 years for women compared with 58 and 62 respectively in 1931. Though desirable, longevity is associated with chronic medical conditions, cancer and a greater need for health and social care.

5.2.4 Lifestyle issues and the NHS

Although the public wants a comprehensive health service, it also appreciates that not all effective treatments should be funded from the public purse. Lifestyle issues such as male baldness and tattoos do not constitute ill health as serious as diabetes or cancer, and it is argued, should be paid for privately (New 2000).

However lifestyle issues can lead to serious medical and social problems. Life time health care costs would be lower if obesity and smoking were prevented before surgery for heart attacks and lung cancer become necessary. That would be limiting personal choice!

5.3 Patient advocacy hurts business

The Association of Community Health Councils (ACHC) commissioned a report on corporate management of the NHS. The report recommended the establishment of an autonomous NHS with a charter and constitution on the lines of the BBC (Hutton 2000).

The Hutton report was published several months before The NHS Plan. So, the NHS the Plan recommended abolishing the vocal Community Health Councils.

5.3.1 Muzzling local opposition

Community health councils (CHCs) were established in 1974 to represent the interests of the public in health services:

- to monitor the operation of local health services,
- to give advice to health authorities, and
- to be consulted about substantial changes in services.

CHCs had the right to inspect NHS health care premises, but were required to obtain the owners' consent before inspecting GP premises.

5.3.2 A crowd of patient advocates

The functions of the CHC were split between a Patient Advocacy Liaison Service (PALS), an Independent Complaints and Advocacy Services (ICAS), a Patient and Public Involvement Forum (PIF) and an Overview and Scrutiny Committee (OSC). These quangos fall under the Commission for Patient and Public Involvement in Healthcare (CPPIH) as enacted by the *National Health Service*

Reform and Health Care Professions Act 2002.

The ***Patient Advocacy Liaison Service*** (PALS) is accountable to the trust board and is administered by the hospital or primary care trust to:

- resolve problems on the spot;
- provide information about local health services to patients, carers and their families and to connect people with local support groups;
- tell people about complaints procedures and direct them to ICAS
- monitor trends in services, inform trusts and PPIFs, make reports to trust management and include its recommendations and the trust's response in an annual 'trust patient prospectus' (HOC Health Committee, July 2003).

The ***Patient and Public Involvement Forum*** (PPIF)'s legal powers include the right to go where patients go, enter all buildings NHS patients use; refer concerns to local authority Overview and Scrutiny Committees; appoint a PPIF member as a non-executive director on trust board; and raise concerns with senior managers or with CPPIH.

Based in every hospital and primary care trust, the PPIF is supposed to be the vehicle for the public to influence strategic priorities and routine local health service management. The PPIF is accountable to CPPIH and will be administered by voluntary organisations on contract to CPPIH. The quango is expected to:

- be the main vehicle for the public to influence strategic priorities and routine management of local health services

- be an independent critic of health care issues and environmental health in their communities

- review services from the patient's perspective and monitor the responses of local health services to patient complaints.

The ***Independent Complaints and Advocacy Service*** (ICAS) is a statutory body charged with helping people with complaints:

- assist people with complaints about health services– hospital, health centre, GP, dentist, pharmacist, optician and ambulance services
- offer independent, free and confidential advisory services
- not judge complaint but assist the complaints process
- communicate recurring issues to OSC.

Based in local councils, the ***Overview and Scrutiny Committee*** (OSC) is a statutory body established to:

- enable councillors to scrutinise local healthcare and
- form Independent Reconfiguration Panels to consider the merits of contested local NHS reorganisations

The ***Commission for Patient and Public Involvement in Healthcare*** (CPPIH) is a statutory quango set up to champion patient concerns in the NHS:

- ensure that NHS services take proper account of patient views
- report to secretary of state for health on how well patient and public involvement scheme is working
- set standards and guidelines for PPIFs and ICAS and accredit training.

5.3.3 Multiple advocates may confuse patients

How will individuals decide which quango to approach with concerns? Most problems will probably go to PALS. Many individuals will fail to distinguish between PALS, PPIF, ICAS and OSC. It is illuminating when a government minister with the remit for local representation in the NHS appears confused about the difference between PALS, ICAS and PPIF–quangos he is charged with setting up.

For a Minister charged with securing better patient and public involvement in healthcare, we are dismayed that at our evidence session ...... failed to grasp the subtle but extremely important distinctions between the organisations which his Government is currently setting up (HOC Health committee, July 2003).

PALS will, it is promised, advise on access to hospital services and complaints within hospital and primary care trusts. ICAS will focus on providing advocacy for patients who wish to pursue complaints. OSC will enable elected local councillors to scrutinise the local NHS.

5.3.4 Foundation hospital board to run patient advocacy

Apparently patient advocacy in foundation hospitals will not be provided by PALS, ICAS, PPIF or OSC as in the rest of the NHS, but by hospital boards. Community Health Councils were abolished, government claimed, because a single body could not, without conflict:

- monitor the operation of local health services,
- give advice to health authorities, and
- be consulted about substantial changes in local services.

Apparently foundation hospital boards will achieve what CHCs were judged incapable of doing- perform the three roles without conflict. Is it because the majority on foundation hospital boards will represent private business that these boards will have the wisdom and skill denied CHCs?

5.3.5 Fear of independent advocates hurting business

Foundation hospitals are designed to usher the NHS into commercial healthcare markets. Statutory patient advocacy would hamper their managers' business freedoms. Foundation hospital trust boards need not waste time over such issues as accountability, equity and 'value for money' that interest local residents and borough councillors.

The Commons Health Committee (July 2003) put the parallel patient advocacy systems to uncoordinated planning at the DH rather than deliberate government policy:

As it is we are left with the impression that some policy within the Department of Health is formulated in total isolation from other policy, leading to the ridiculous situation the NHS and its patients are now faced with the introduction of two parallel but entirely different systems of patient and public involvement within the NHS within one year (HOC Health committee, July 2003)

5.4 Deficiencies in corporate leadership

Despite the overwhelming popularity of the NHS and the dedication of its staff, two major issues, finance and management, have dominated the life of the service. Funding problems are made worse by medical advances. Until recently there was no framework for evaluating discoveries before incorporating them into the NHS. The National Institute for Clinical Excellence (NICE) is expected to fill perform the assess new 'products' and services.

Availability of management expertise has not kept pace with the expansion and sophistication of health care. There is constant uncertainty about the future direction of the service. Before fund holding took root, it was changed to locality commissioning. Hospital trusts must become "foundation hospitals" before they have developed adequate skills and staff to manage their services and budgets.

These changes are introduced in full knowledge of the shortage of skilled personnel. Why the hurry?

In its report on foundation hospitals, the Health Select Committee has expressed major concerns over the "*Financial implications*, *Staffing implications*, *Governance and accountability*, *Impact on quality of management and quality of patient care* and *Impact on the wider NHS"* (HOC Health Select committee 2003).

Alan Milburn, secretary of state for health, resigned before responding to the Health Select Committee's report.

*Dr Eccles, deputy chair of the BMA junior doctors' committee, said the resignation had been greeted by cheers in his hospital... ...he has created an NHS that is more politicised than at any time before and...centred around making politicians looking good... (*Hall 2003).

Friends of the NHS hope that John Reid, the new secretary of sate, will introduce better researched reforms whose impact on the whole service will be thought through before they are implemented.

5.5 Why is government shrinking the NHS?

In the 1990s, the Conservatives claimed that the NHS was inefficient in the use of resources and introduced measures to '*improve*' efficiency. The DH imposed a 6% capital charge on hospitals to remind NHS managers of what the assets would cost if they were rented from the private sector. It was neither to reflect the real cost of capital to government, nor to improve patient care. Why was it necessary? Perhaps, it is preparing the NHS for a time when such property will be rented from the private sector.

5.5.1 Financing games favour privatisation

In 1998-99 capital charges worth £2,991m were '*collected*' from the NHS, '*returned*' to the Treasury and then '*used to fund*' the NHS (DH 2000). Aligning NHS capital accounting with the private sector disguises differences between the private and public sectors and makes eventual privatisation of health services easier to sell to the public (Pollock and Gaffney 1998; Shaoul 1998).

The DH requires the NHS to make 'efficiency savings' in administrative and clinical activities. Hospital trusts are directed to increase productivity (number of patients seen or treated) by 3% per year without extra resources (Warden 1996). Initially many hospital trusts made the savings, but soon reached the limits of their efficiency.

The 3% annual efficiency target may also encourage.... trusts to look for easy short term methods to improve efficiency without regard to the long term effects.....incentive to increase activity in hospital and a disincentive.... to shift resources into ... primary care (Dixon and Harrison 1997)

Many NHS trusts have met efficiency savings by cutting services and/ or not filling vacant staff positions. Financial targets were met, but the service shrunk.

5.5.2 PFI shrinks NHS capacity faster

Capital charges and efficiency savings did not shrink hospitals fast enough, so the private finance initiative (see 7.8) was accelerated. Trusts were directed to use a 6% discount rate when comparing public sector with PFI funding.

Governments can borrow at 3% to 4%. PFI projects are rented at 9 - 18 % of construction cost. Why must the NHS accept such an expensive financing when public funding would be more than 60% cheaper (Pollock et al 1999)?

5.5.3 The efficiency trap

NHS managers initially accepted the need for efficiency savings. Over time they became concerned as efficiency drives led to inefficiency, poor patient care, low staff morale and patient dissatisfaction. It looks as if capital charges and efficiency saving were meant to downsize hospital services (Beecham 1996, BMA 2001).

NHS managers have no power to protect their trusts from the deleterious impact of capital charges and efficiency savings. They are public employees whose pay and future is determined by how well they obey DH directives.

The NHS has no means of objecting to any reform however ill advised they may be. It has no power to makes policies of its own; it only follows directives (Hutton 2000).

5.6 Why is the NHS short of native nurses?

The NHS is not free to pay its workers the market rate for the job. Decisions about NHS pay are made by politicians, who also are in charge of controlling inflation and limiting taxes increases

The nurse's salary bill (at £7.6 billion in 1999) is prominently large. Politicians use public control pay to restrict government expenditure. Their dilemma is pay nurses and other public servants a descent wage, raise taxes to meet the salary bill and risk higher inflation as well as losing the next general election. Or, restrain public sector pay, ensure low taxation, lose native NHS nurses, but win the next general election. Of course politicians prefer winning elections.

5.6.1 Nurses' salaries are poor

The main cause of shortage of native nurses is poor pay. The nurse's starting salary is lower than that of the school teacher and police constable. Difference in the pay of these public servants widens with length of service (Box 5.2).

Box 5.2: Salary of a newly qualified nurse, school teacher and police constable; if not promoted

Cadre	Starting	% > nurse	After 4 years	% > nurse
Staff nurse	£14,890	--	£16,445	--
School teacher	£15,537	4.3%	£19,407	18.0%
Police constable	£17,133	15.1%	£21,567	31.1%

RCN 2000 (www.rcn.org.uk)

Most modern nurses are less meek than their predecessors. They are aware of the size of salaries earned in the private sector by workers with similar qualifications. Graduate nurses leave the NHS when the spirit for public service is not sustained by an income sufficient to pay the house mortgage.

"Staff have mortgages and bills to pay and they will seek work elsewhere. Pay overall is a major problem in regard to recruitment" (R Dobson 1999).

5.6.2 NHS steals nurses from the 3rd world

The NHS watches powerlessly as health professionals leave for better rewards in the private sector. It has resorted to recruiting nurses from poorer countries of the 3rd World.

"We are very disappointed that as a country we are unable to recruit nurses, to bring staffing levels up to those required. At the same time we are also depriving other countries...." said Mike Colley, UNISON organiser in Wales after the arrival of Filipino nurse recruits (Dobson 1999).

5.6.3 Why pay rises have failed to retain nurses

The government has little chance of stemming the exodus of native nurses from the NHS; not with the pay rises of 3.7% (Grice and Lawrance 2000).

After the 2000-01 pay was announced, a grade D nurse in Gasteshead said the 3.7 % rise meant only £11 more per week and that it was an insult to the work nurses do and a barrier to attracting more people into the profession:

"I love nursing, I love my job, but I can't say that I will still be in

the post in five years. There are many jobs with much better salaries for half the work.

"There are 22,000 nursing vacancies in this country and the Government are supposed to be trying to fill these. With a pay rise like this they have no chance" (Foster 2000).

To bring the nurse's starting pay to that of the police constable would require a 15.1% and not 3.7% pay rise.

5.6.4 The nurse's career has slowed down

The second reason for the shortage of native nurses is that their NHS careers are progressing very slowly or not at all. Promotions have been reduced by the internal market and cash starved trusts. In 2000 just over half of all nurses were at the top of their salary scales. The most senior three clinical grades (Grades G, H and I) had shrunk by over 13% in the previous eight years (RCN 2000).

Senior nursing sisters, health visitors and district nurses (Grade G), the very nurses expected to act as 'modern matrons' are the most affected. Many cash strapped hospital trusts have not filled senior nursing positions when incumbents retire. They hire lower grade nurses or leave positions unfilled– often to meet the 3% efficiency savings.

At the time when government had announced plans to expand nurses' duties and responsibilities, the number of senior nurses in post had fallen by 9,000. Some nurses who had hoped to be promoted into the lost posts are leaving the NHS (RCN 2000).

5.6.5 NNS does not encourage older nurses to stay

Older nurses *"feel they are being ignored and neglected and are opting for early retirement"* (BBC News 23 July 20030). NHS nurses are aging– at least 75,000 are over 55 years old and 71,000 are between 50-54 years. A growing number are taking early retirement; about 10,000 nurses retire each year. A small number return to nursing.

"Attitudes to older nurses are sometimes ambivalent, sometimes apathetic and sometimes welcoming. Some older nurses reported ageist attitudes towards them by employers and their personnel departments, although employers also valued particular qualities that they associated with older nurses" (Watson et al. 2003).

5.7 Where do specialists come from?

Medical specialties and royal medical colleges develop from the efforts of medical special interest groups who are eventually granted royal charters to become royal medical colleges.

First there were the royal colleges of physicians (physic = *the art or practice of healing*) in London, Edinburgh and Glasgow, then the royal college of surgeons (descendants of barbers who cut hair and lanced boils). Other colleges (obstetrics, general practice, ophthalmology, pathology, radiology, paediatrics and child health, and anaesthetics) followed.

Royal medical colleges develop from the efforts of special interest medical groups who organise and promote their interest. Like the British Paediatric Association (BPA), formed in 1928, they organise meetings, share new knowledge and practices, encourage and publish research, and become the voice for their special interest. Eventually they get known and respected as experts in their specialism.

Eventually the association, faculty or society applies to the Privy Council for a royal charter (permit) authorising them to practice their art under the protection of the monarch– to become a royal college. The BPA became the Royal College of Paediatrics and Child Health (RCPCH) in 1996. The journey can be protracted; 58 years, it took the BPA to become the RCPCH.

5.7.1 Government not interested in birth of specialties

I am not aware that at any stage in the development of a medical specialty, the DH actively assists the work of interest groups or converses for the creation of new specialties. Even in established specialties, the DH does not encourage, nor facilitate the training of sufficient specialists.

5.7.2 Efficiency savings create shortage of specialists

Lord Hunt of Kings Health: My Lords, there is no doubt that pathologists have an extremely valuable role to play in the National Health Service. There has been concerns in relation to shortages... (Lords Hansard, 4 June 2000)

Earl Howe: My Lords, is the Minister aware that in some parts of the country, breast screening services have been suspended because of shortage of radiologists? What is being done to tackle that...(Lords Hansard, 7 Jan 2003).

The shortage of pathologists and radiologists was preventable. Traditionally the salary of a hospital junior doctor (senior house officer, or SHO) is shared between the hospital employing the doctor and the regional postgraduate dean (a government medical training office). In pathology and radiology, SHOs take time, about 3 years, before they are skilled enough to report on pathology material or on X-rays.

So hospital trusts would not employ them– that would be spending money on unproductive staff. With a *'3% efficiency savings'* directive hanging over their heads, this was understandable. Postgraduate deans would not meet the full SHO salary either. The DH left the problem to be *solved by local mechanisms*.

So, for a number of years fewer than (*planned*) pathologists and radiologists were trained. It was only after hospitals started scrambling to fill posts– paying salary premiums– that the DH eventually agreed to fund the full SHO salary for trainees in pathology and radiology.

5.7.2 Shortage of professionals to continue

Shortages of health professionals of different cadres are common, almost characteristics of some services. This was highlighted recently by news of shortage of specialists in allergy (RCP 2003, *Sky News* 2003). There has always been a shortage of specialist in allergy and of specialists in many clinical disciplines (Box 5.3). It was fortunate the RCP report caught the interest of the press. Many equally important reports die without the public ever hearing about their contents.

Many disciplines have always been short of trained personnel. No plans to remedy the shortages have been announced.

Box 5.3: Healthcare disciplines short of trained professionals	
Services for children	**Services for adults**
Allergy	Allergy and asthma
Behavioural disorders	Epilepsy and neurology
Communications disorders	Geriatric nursing
Dermatology	Histopathology
Epilepsy and neurology	Learning disability
Histopathology	Psychiatric nursing
Learning disorders	Psycho-geriatrics
Mental health nursing	Psychiatry
Nursing (paediatric, newborn)	Occupational therapy
Occupational therapy	Physical disability
Physiotherapy	Physiotherapy
Psychology and psychiatry	Radiology
Radiology	Rehabilitation medicine
Speech and Language	Speech and Language
etc.	**etc.**

5.7.3 DH should assist shortage disciplines

Unglamourous disciplines will remain short of professionals unless the DH gets involved in emergency midwifery– pays better salaries, provides better facilities (buildings, equipment) and funds adequate support services (child and adult mental health, physical and learning disability, etc), etc.

Will the PMETB enhance specialism?

It is expected that the proposed Postgraduate Medical Education and Training Board (PMETB) will give the NHS a clear say in the training of doctors and increase patient representation and influence. PMETB membership shall include doctors, patients and NHS representatives.

The *"Postgraduate Medical Education and Training - A Paper for Consultation: The Medical Education Standards Board,"* was published in December 2000 and gives duties of the PMETB as:

- supervising UK postgraduate medical education, setting standards and ensuring that training meets requirements

- approving training and assessing whether doctors have completed training satisfactorily

- issuing certificates of satisfactory completion of training

- maintaining a register of doctors entitled to work as specialists or general practitioners in the UK

- assessing the training of doctor from countries that do not satisfy EEA requirements for mutual recognition.

The PMETB will work with royal colleges and faculties to set frameworks and standards of education and training.

The creation and nurturing of new specialties is not mentioned in the consultation document. Or did I miss it?

---

6. Rationing health care

6.1 The NHS is a welfare service

The nationalisation of public services in the 1940s altered social attitudes to welfare. The welfare state aimed to organise the provision of basic physical and economic needs of all residents of the United Kingdom:

- the 1944 *Education Act* established free universal education for all children at primary, secondary and higher levels

- the *Family Allowances Act* introduced universal child allowance payment for each child up to leaving school

- the 1946 *National Insurance Act* and the *National Industrial Injuries Act* provided protection against loss of income

- the 1946 *National Health Service Act* provided access to health care free of charge at the point of use.

However the principle of free welfare services funded from general taxation has been eroded:

- charging for dentures and spectacles started in 1951, and charging for drug prescriptions was imposed in 1952
- university fees have been introduced and will grow
- care of the elderly is almost fully privatised (DH 2000).

6.2 Access to health care

The objectives of a national health service are maximising health gain by improving access and enhancing the quality of services (Benatar 1996, New 1996).

Access to universal health care has been achieved in most developed countries except the USA where individuals must take out personal medical insurance. The uninsured, mainly the poor, the unemployed or the chronically sick, have no guaranteed access to health care (Benatar 1996). Because of rapid increases in healthcare costs and to imitate USA social policy, many countries are privatising healthcare.

6.2.1 Maximising health gain

Maximising health gain means that health promotion, disease prevention and curative health care are used to attain the best possible outcome– higher life expectancy, as little disability as possible, and a pain-free life.

Reducing health inequalities means that some localities, groups or individuals might receive more help than others. It has been claimed (Webster 1998) that although the gap in the health status between the top and lower social classes in the UK widened under Conservative governments, the health of the nation is much better than it would have been if there were no NHS. Probably.

6.2.2 Access to adequate health care

Access to health care and continuing improvement in the health of deprived areas, groups or individuals should be the aim of a public health service. The NHS aims to provide equal access based on medical need. There is a fair amount of accountability to the public and a system for investigating complaints. However there are long waiting lists for hospital treatment. While in Germany access is virtually instant, it spends a higher proportion of her GDP on health care than the UK.

6.2.3 Quality of services

The quality of NHS services is considered adequate for the level of funding. However mortality from cancer and heart diseases is higher in Britain than in Germany where more money is spent on healthcare. Low investment in health services has delayed the establishment of effective treatments for these and other conditions.

The Labour government has pledged higher funding for the NHS; extra money for cancer and heart disease has been promised.

"... the Secretary of State for Health, unveiled an extra £100m investment in cancer and heart services ....to tackle what he described as the "greatest priorities" for the NHS. An extra £87.5m is to go to....cancers of the stomach, pancreas and oesophagus (gullet)" (Laurence 2001).

The standard of cleanliness in NHS hospitals is considered to be poor. Conservative public sector reforms during the 1980s and 1990s privatised hospital cleaning. The privatisation has been blamed for the low standard of cleanliness and outbreaks of antibiotic resistant infections (*Independent* 9 Jan 2001).

For a time, the DH instructed hospitals to spend every penny on direct patient care and not on infrastructure. Recently the DH has punished hospitals, through star ratings, for crumbling buildings (Bosely 2001).

Ten hospitals in England were yesterday named and shamed as facing the biggest struggle to meet cleanliness targets by the health secretary.

The drive to clean up hospitals..... an effort to reduce the number of infections in hospital, which affect 100,000 people a year, kill 5,000 and cost the NHS about £1bn to treat.

Competitive tendering for hospital cleaning contracts has also been scrapped, because low prices have resulted in lower standards (Bosely 2001).

The government announced the cleanliness drive, scrapping of competitive tendering for hospital cleaning and money to help hospitals clean up a few weeks before the 2001 general elections.

When competitive tendering was imposed, the Conservative government was warned that the quality of cleaning would decline. NHS staff were reassured that performance contracts and market forces would ensure superior and cheaper cleaning services– *'value for money.*

6.3.4 Reduced role of public preventive measures

Current government policies do not emphasise health promotion and prevention. The Health Education Authority was abolished in the 1990s and its remit has eventually been assumed by the Health Development Agency (HDA) which *"identifies the evidence of what works to improve people's health and reduce health inequalities"*.

Health promotion and preventive health measures were left to personal choice and market forces.

Government fear of destroying the beef market caused delay in implementing measures to prevent the spread of Mad Cow Disease to humans. Even after people had died of new variant Creutzfeldt-Jacob disease, the human form of the disease, measures for reducing transmission to humans were poorly enforced (Wise 1996).

6.3 Rationing in the NHS

Since the birth of the NHS limiting access to services (rationing) has been used to control demand. In 1951 the demand for dentures and spectacle was so greater that charging was introduced to ration them by 'ability to pay'. Prescription charges were introduced in 1952 to raise revenue (Webster 1991). The 'waiting list' is a standard tool for rationing resources in education, council housing, health care or any other service or product, when demand exceeds supply.

6.3.1 Euphemisms for rationing

'Rationing' implies limited resources, exclusion or denial of a service to individuals. In health care rationing means limiting access or withholding treatment or resources.

'Priority setting' relates to services or client groups, and involves choosing between what should (or should not) be done or provided.

Politicians hate the word 'rationing' and both Conservatives and Labour governments have used euphemisms for rationing– *'priority setting'*, *'resource allocation'*, *'ring fenced budgets'*, *'earmarked monies'* in political debate and government directives (New 1996).

Priority setting and *resource allocation* depend on value judgements, while rationing is based on scarcity of resources.

6.3.2 The rationing debate

The rationing debate has been dominated by political assertions and hardly any dispassionate analyses of issues (Mills and Heaton 1991, Frankel and West 1993). It is often promoted on false premises (New 1996, Frankel et al 2000, Murray 2000) as reducing wastage or limiting costs. The rationing debate could be summarised as follows:

Political assertions rather than analysis of issues

The rationing debate has hardly included epidemiological, economic and financial analyses of the actual demand and supply for services. No data are given on the adequacy and efficiency of management structures (New 1996).

Imbalance between supply and demand not demonstrated

Possible imbalances between supply and demand have not been separated from central corporate mismanagement. No evidence has been produced in terms of *'return on investment'* (health preservation and gain) in relation to spending on health care; nor *'return on management'* (which management systems are most efficient and effective) for the amount of resources employed (Mills and Heaton 1991).

6.3.3 Blaming NHS staff for inadequate services

Governments have attributed NHS deficiencies to the self interest of health professionals (doctors) and not to an excess of demand over available resources.

Conservative and Labour *spin-doctors* work tirelessly to shift blame for the ills of the NHS from government to NHS staff:

- *long waiting lists are caused by mismanagement–* private sector managers were recruited to run hospitals, but waiting lists continued to grow

- *budget overspends are caused by extravagance–* a 6% capital charge, a 3% 'efficiency savings' and an internal market were imposed, but hospital trusts continued to' *over spend*'.

There is ample evidence that as a group, NHS professionals deliver services more cheaply and effectively than the private sector (Webster 1998, Hutton 2000).

Hospitals are unfairly reprimanded for overspending. The hospital's offence has been treating more patients than was budgeted for. NHS budgets are guestimates. Nobody knows exactly how many patients will, next year, enter the hospital looking for treatment.

6.3.4 Promoting rationing as socially neutral

Rationing debates are sharper during recessions when making *"choices"* sounds plausible. The debate includes phrases like *'setting priorities'*, making *'hard choices'*, '*value for money*', and '*efficiency savings'*. However it is not agreed as to who should be treated and who should be denied care (Ham 1998).

6.3.5 A rationed core service?

Government could offer access to a limited list of cost effective treatments and procedures in response to need and medical advances. Difficulties arise in defining conditions and treatments to include or exclude in the package (Ham 1998).

Advocates of 'reduce and ration' are unable to specify what to exclude. Varicose veins, extraction of wisdom teeth and cosmetic surgery are often named. These account for less than 0.5% of the NHS budget. Big money goes to childbirth, elderly care, cancer, heart disease, and mental health (Coast 1997, Doyal 1997). Which of these should be rationed?

By identifying treatments that are not cost-effective, NICE is expected to help free financial resources for more cost-effective interventions (DH 2000).

6.4 Waiting list '*crises*'

Waiting for services has been part of the NHS since its birth. Demand for dentures and spectacles was so high, and waiting lists so long, that charging was introduced in 1951 to limit demand (*rationing by ability to pay*) and to raise revenue. Aneurin Bevan, NHS founding minister of health (secretary of state), resigned over the breach of the basic NHS principle of '*a health service free of charge at the point of use*' (Webster 1991).

Impact of waiting list on patient care

After studying the impact of waiting lists on patient care Murray (2000) reached a number of conclusions:

- delays occur in healthcare systems, cause discontent, consume resources and worsen clinical outcomes
- most waiting systems rely on distinguishing between urgent and

- most waiting systems rely on distinguishing between urgent and routine cases and so maintain two queues

- improving access involves determining the demand and providing resources to meet the demand; or reducing it

- real improvements in access occur when there is one short queue that ensures prompt treatment for urgent cases.

6.5 Waiting list initiatives

It is only recently that the length of a '*waiting list*' has become a '*political crisis*'. Politicians have responded by setting up '*waiting list initiatives*' under which surgical teams are employed to reduce the size of the waiting list– but not to prevent it from growing again.

Waiting list initiatives distort service priorities (Mills and Heaton 1991, Frankel and West 1993; Frankel et al 2000).

Non-surgical conditions (heart disease, diabetes, hypertension, sexual health, learning disability, etc) do not usually figure in waiting list initiatives, even if they affect decisions about surgery (cardiology services determine need for revascularisation surgery in ischaemic heart disease).

6.6 Manipulating waiting lists

Too many variables impact on the size of hospital waiting lists for them to be reliable, fair or objective criteria on which to base the performance of a hospital trust and its managers (Torrington and Hall managers.

The government's obsession with waiting times and performance targets is making "honest people dishonest", damaging patient care and leading to fiddled figures on how well the NHS is doing, Dr Ian Bogle, chairman of the British Medical Association, said yesterday (Timmins 2003).

Following an inquiry into allegations that South Warwickshire General Hospitals NHS Trust had deceitfully altered its waiting lists, its chief executive resigned:

"After due consideration, Mr Riley has decided to resign from his position as chief executive to seek new opportunities elsewhere...(Hazlewood 2001).

Liam Fox, shadow Health Secretary, commented:

"Up and down the country, waiting lists have been fiddled to suit the Government's purposes..... The public will expect other chief executives who have been fiddling waiting list figures to follow Mr Riley's example" (Hazlewood 2001).

Waiting list initiatives do not prevent cancer, stop old ladies breaking hip bones or banish heart attacks. Natural disease cycles continue irrespective of waiting list initiatives.

What is needed is a balanced supply of services to meet demand; not episodic initiatives. If capacity and access do not increase to meet demand, waiting list initiatives are futile.

Dr Bogle, who is a member of the government's NHS Modernisation Board, added: "You would think that the government would be distancing itself from these corrupt and immoral practices." Instead, it has turned a blind eye, been triumphalist about its achievements and colluded in the deception and the double speak" (Timmins 2003).

Growing surgical capacity

Capacity for surgery is recovering through *"Growing Capacity: Independent sector diagnosis and treatment centres"* (DH, 2002). These '*centres*' are simple but glorified, privatized surgical wards.

What is the future of conditions for which there are undocumented but long waits for treatment (child mental health, learning disability, sexual health, psychiatry, etc) or services are grossly inadequate (see Box 5.3)? None– they are not marketable to the private sector.

6.7 Rationing is inevitable

Politicians should communicate the inevitability of rationing without diminishing public faith in what is provided (New, 1996).

"The concept of the NHS as a comprehensive service may have outlived its usefulness. It will be increasingly commonplace to see treatments which are judged to be of limited clinical... effectiveness....excluded from this system (BMA 2001).

6.7.1 Fear of losing office

When Labour accused the Conservative party of deliberately damaging the NHS, fear of losing the general election prompted

Margaret Thatcher to declare that "*the NHS is safe in our hands*' (Whitney 1998).

Higher taxes reduce the electability of political parties, so politicians strive to avoid raising taxes. Labour favours covert taxation to avoid the curse of '*the party of high taxation*'.

6.7.2 The NHS needs overt rationing

Publicly funded health services cannot be delivered without rationing. The issue is how rationing should be managed (Whitehead 1994). Rationing should be open so that the public has the opportunity to influence the way decisions are made (Doyal 1997).

It is easy to call for public debate on rationing but difficult to agree what should and should not be rationed. The state of Oregon (USA) could not agree on what to ration despite well publicised, but poorly attended public debates (Ham 1998).

It is better to be open about the difficulties of rationing than risk the political consequences of deceiving the public. Rationing is difficult to manage to everyone's satisfaction. Explicit principles do not codify behaviour, but only create moral boundaries within which decisions are taken.

Rationing is inevitable and pervades the NHS. It awaits public acknowledgement of its existence.

---

7. Privatising health care

7.1 Privatising the welfare state

In the 1980s and 90s Tory governments publicly privatised many public enterprises (gas, steel, coal, telecommunications, railways, council houses and many others).

Public and private sector provision of essential services is summarised in Box 7.1. Public services (local councils, the NHS, education and even the armed forces) were forced to privatise support services and staff housing, to charge market rates for staff housing and to sell empty land. Public employees were transferred from public sector occupational pensions to private pension schemes, often against strong opposition.

Privatisation of welfare state has been achieved by:

- transferring public service infrastructure, assets and some workforces to the private sector through PFI projects
- using the concordat with the private sector to include private hospitals and nursing homes into NHS healthcare provision
- creating primary care trusts are ordering them to 'buy' health services from NHS providers as well as the private sector; and
- establishing foundation hospitals with powers to participate in health care markets on commercial terms

Box 7.1: Public and private sector provision of essential services

Public sector	*Semi-autonomous*	*Private sector*
Health • Hospital trusts • Primary care trusts	• Royal medical colleges • GMC, NMC, etc • NHS quangos: CHAI, NCAA, NICE, Medicine Agency, etc • Foundation hospitals?	• Private hospital • Private insurance • Company insurance • NHS infrastructure • Catering • Some Lab. services
Education • Local authority schools • Higher education • State universities	• Maintained schools • Technical colleges • Endowed universities	• Private schools • Private colleges • Private universities
Housing • Municipal/ council	• Housing associations • Housing action trusts • Occupational housing	• Owner-occupier • Private rented • Employer housing
Financial benefits • Basic national pension • Child allowance • Sickness/invalidity pay	• Occupational pension • Sick pay	• Private pensions • Life insurance • Income protection.

Extension of Coxall and Robins, 1998

- abolition of universal student grants, establishment of student loans schemes and finally the introduction of university tuition fees,

- through new regulatory quangos– CHAI to inspect and license independent health care providers and NICE to determine which treatments should be provided on the NHS.

7.2. Privatising education

University tuition is being privatised in small doses– first abolish universal student grants, then introduce a small tuition charge, gradually increase the charge till the full cost is paid by the student– American style. University tuition charges started around £1000 per annum and will 'grow'.

Labour MPs are beginning to appreciate that one of the pillars of the welfare state– free education from primary to university level– is under attack. When government proposed that some universities could charge large amounts, there was a small revolt of Labour backbenchers. Had all disaffected MPs voted against the motion instead of abstaining, the government would have lost the vote (Beattie and Hardie 2003).

7.3 Agenda for privatising the NHS

In 1987 a conference of Conservative politicians, senior NHS officials, and members of a *"new right"* think-tank produced a seven point programme for transforming the NHS (Box 7.2; Hart 1994).

The reforms the agenda gave birth to were promoted as measures to improve the quality, accessibility, and efficiency of the NHS. Market forces were hailed as a sure means of improving quality and efficiency. An internal market was created against opposition from the public and NHS staff.

Conservative governments proclaimed reverence for the principles of the NHS while injecting market practices and dishonesty into the service (Hart 1994). Although Tories lost the 1997 elections, destabilisation of the NHS has accelerated under Labour reforms.

Box 7.2: 1987 Conservative agenda for privatising the NHS

1. *Establish the NHS as an independent statutory body with decentralised financial accountability;*
2. *Integrate the NHS and private medical care into an interrelated market;*
3. *Extend direct charging in a costed service;*
4. *Devolve all responsibility for patients' care to directly funded district health authorities, dismantle regional health authorities and their planning function, encourage individual hospitals to opt out and to compete for patients;*
5. *End national wage bargaining for NHS staff;*
6. *Rename the NHS to reflect a new business era;*
7. *Jointly, with private insurance companies, create a national health insurance scheme.*

Hart 1994

7.4 Labour adopts Tory agenda

Although it won the 1997 general election with a big majority, Labour did not renationalise public utilities.

A number of rail accidents and poor performance by *Railtrack* were blamed on the privatisation of *British Rail*. These incidents forced the government to take over Railtrack and change it into *Network Rail*, a '*not for profit organisation'*. Yes– it loses money and survives on a public subsidy. However, Labour continues with plans to privatise the London Underground!

Labour did not reverse Conservative health care reforms. It adopted some, slightly modified others and introducing many of its own.

Labour accidentally prepares NHS for privatisation

Although most Britons do not expect Labour to privatise the NHS, recent reforms have created a strong fear, an expectation, that when Tories return to government (when Labour loses a general election), the NHS will be ready for privatisation:

- the NHS internal market continues through locality 'commissioning' of health services from private and NHS providers

- charging for health services continues unabated and has been reinforced by the introduction '*Reforming NHS Financial Flows: Introducing payment by results* (DH 2002)

- elderly care has been scaled down, means tested and privatised; only 'nursing care' is said to be funded– but difficult to separate personal care from 'nursing care' in frail individuals

- successive governments have encouraged self medication and private prescriptions (Heath 1994)

- the 6% charge (tax) on NHS capital funding, introduced by the

Conservatives, continues and Labour made it a compulsory comparator of public versus PFI funding of capital projects

- the *Concordat* paved the way for building Diagnosis and Treatment Centres for private firms to exploit (DH 2002)

- when established, foundation hospitals will integrated the NHS into healthcare markets.

7.5 Charging for health care

Charging for services has grown faster than inflation. For non-exempt individuals subsidy for health care has declined. Charging for health care (Box 7.3) is inconsistent with NHS founding philosophy of "*free health care at the time of delivery*" (Birch 1986).

Box 7.3: Examples of Prescription charges, 1 April 2002

Item	Charge in April 2001 (£)	Charge in April 2002 (£)
Prescription Charge (PC)	6.10	6.20
4 months Prepaid PC	31.90	32.40
12 months Prepaid PC	87.60	89.00
Surgical Bra	20.60	20.90
Spinal/abdominal support	31.00	31.50
Wig Acrylic	50.70	51.50
Wig Partial Human Hair	133.70	135.90
Wig Full Human Hair	195.40	198.60

DH, Pharmacy and Prescriptions Branch, March 2002

7.5.1 Charging for dentures and spectacles

Charging for dentures and spectacles was followed by quiet privatisation of dental and ophthalmic care. Eye sight tests are paid privately, except for children under 16 years, glaucoma and diabetes suffers. Spectacles are free to exempt groups.

As ophthalmic and dental services were privatised their use declined. There is concern that among poor but non-exempt groups, poor vision, cataracts and glaucoma may not be detected till after vision has been damaged (Appleby, 1992).

7.5.2 Prescription charges

The prescription charge, introduced in 1952 to raise revenue and restrain demand has grown faster than inflation from 5p per item in 1952 to 630p in 2003 (12,500%).

Restraining demand for health care has echoes of '*economy and deterrence*' and the workhouse. Demand is restrained by covert rationing of access (the 5 minute GP consultation, waiting for treatment, inadequate hospital capacity, and shortage of essential professionals).

Exemption from charges

Since 1968 certain individuals have been exempted from prescription charges (Box 7.4). Nevertheless a number of chronic conditions (arthritis, asthma, bronchitis and hypertension) that require life-long treatment are not exempt. Why? Because they are common! Hypertension, like diabetes, asthma and chronic arthritis, is common.

....29 million adults in the five countries—13% of the population—

have blood pressure above 160/95 mm Hg, and another 46 million (21%) have blood pressure in the range 140/90 to 160/95. ... most European countries specify target levels of 140 mm Hg systolic and 90 mm Hg diastolic pressure (Dobson 2002).

Box 7.4: Examples of exemptions from prescription charges	
Age related Children under 16 years Under 19, in full time education People over 60 years of age **Permanent fistulae** Caecostomy, Colostomy Ileostomy, Laryngostomy **People entitled to remission** Income support, Family credit, Disability working allowance, Job seekers allowance, Working family credit, etc. **Other situations** Contraceptive services Epilepsy, on anti-epilepsy drugs War pension exemption certificates	**Exemption certificates holders** Expectant mothers, Women who have born a child or stillbirth in last 12 months **Hormonal disorders** Addison disease, hypopituitarism, and diabetes insipidus, insulin dependent diabetes, myasthenia gravis, hyperthyroidism, hypothyroidism , etc **Prepayment certificates** Long term medication; payers are eligible to prepay for medicines Continuing physical disability and requiring a carer's help to leave house.

Prescription Pricing Authority 2000

Although 85% of prescriptions are exempt, revenue from the charge has increased (Walley 1998). Prescription charges are expected to raise £446 million in 2003/04 (DH 2002).

The prescription charge, currently £6.30 per item, is not related to the cost of the medicine prescribed. About 60% of drugs dispensed cost less than the charge. It is a simple to collect tax on the use of NHS services.

Charging for prescriptions is intended to deter excessive demand and raise revenue. Its value in deterring usage is limited by the exemption of 85% of prescriptions.

Non-exempt patients are less likely than the exempt to present their prescriptions for dispensing. Increased charges and the consequent fall in dispensed prescriptions imply that charging does inhibit some patients from getting essential treatment.

Is the NHS denying treatment to individuals who are unable to pay prescription charges (Walley 1998)?

Some doctors offer private prescriptions to non-exempt patients when the cost of the drug is less than the charge; or advise them to buy the medicine over the counter.

7.6 Promoting self medication

The NHS spends about 10% of its budget on drugs. Drug costs have increased steadily over recent decades (Freemantle and Bloor 1996, ABPI 2002). Government would like this expenditure to decline or at least to stabilise. Prescription charges raise revenue; but self medication avoids cost of drugs and consultation altogether.

7.6.1 Demand for OTC medicines is growing

Demand for drugs sold over-the-counter (OTC) is increasing. Many factors contribute to the increase (Rogers et al 1998):

- the younger generation are less likely to wait as long, as their grand parents did, for common ailments to heal themselves. They expect rapid relief of symptoms and will buy and use OTC medicine

- politicians often advise people to see their GPs or consult the pharmacist implying that some medicine will be prescribed or an OTC remedy will be recommended

- promotion of OTC remedies by pharmaceutical companies in newspapers, magazines, on television and radio

- the media (magazines and newspapers, the internet, radio and television) promote and often recommend medical remedies. Drugs can be ordered over the internet without prescriptions.

- independent health care providers (herbalists, chiropractors, acupuncturists, homeopaths, osteopaths) are more willing to recommend OTC drugs or other remedies– and clients are happy to buy them

- health care professionals (dentists, doctors, pharmacists, nurses, various physiotherapists etc) may recommend OTC medicines

In 1994, OTC drug market in Britain was £1.27 billion (Box 7.5). Pain killers and remedies for skin, common cold and indigestion accounted for 44% of the revenue (Blenkinsopp and Bradley 1996).

7.6.2 Drug advertisements

Brand promotion is a powerful tool in creating demand for drugs. Patients believe that branded medicines are more potent than their generic versions. The public in general believes '*Neurofen*' is superior to ibuprofen, its generic. Faith is an essential ingredient.

Box 7.5: OTC sales (non-prescription drugs), 1994

Condition	***Sales (£m)***	***% sales***
Pain	196.4	16.7
Skin	143.5	11.3
Cold	93.9	7.4
Indigestion	73.9	5.8
Sore throat	72.7	5.7
Cough	68.1	5.4
Other remedies	620.4	47.7
Total	**1268.9**	(**100**)

After Blenkinsopp and Bradley, 1996

In the 1980s the Conservative government made it easier to move drugs from 'prescription-only' to the OTC category and fuelled demand for OTC medicines.

Advertising prescription-only drugs directly to consumers is expanding in USA. Pharmaceutical companies are pressing authorities in the UK to allow direct promotion of prescription-only drugs to the consumer (Hoffman and Wilkes, 1999).

7.6.3 Abusing OTC medicine

Users appreciate being able to buy OTC medicines without waiting to see their GP first. However people, particularly teenage girls, have used paracetamol and aspirin in attempted suicide. Unfortunately some succeed. The number of tablets of aspirin or paracetamol that can be bought over the counter has been reduced. However the permitted amounts are enough to cause serious harm and death (Cranney et al. 1998).

7.6.4 Will the NHS drug bill stabilise?

New and expensive prescription drugs will lead to higher drug costs and the need for rationing. Cash limited PCTs will be tempted to give private prescriptions and to recommend OTC medicines (Newdick 1998). NHS expenditure on drugs (Box 7.6) continues to grow (ABPI 2002).

Box 7.6: NHS expenditure per person

Year	Total NHS cost £ m	Total NHS cost per person £	Total NHS medicines cost £ m	NHS medicines/ person £	Medicines as a % of total cost
1980	11,257	200	826	37.86	8.9
1985	17,154	303	1,627	47.77	9.8
1990	28,246	448	2,533	60.75	8.9
1995	41,853	680	4,583	91.34	11.0
2000	57,067	878	7,073	120.63	12.4
2001	62,892	955	7,753	129.25	12.3

From ABPI (Association of the British Pharmaceutical Industry), 2002

Private prescriptions and OTC medicines have been encouraged by UK government for decades (Bradley and Blenkinsopp 1996, Hoffman and Wilkes 1999). Governments promote self medication in the belief that it will reduce demand for NHS services. Patients resort to OTC remedies because they are unable to see a GP quickly.

Self medication is a neat way of privatising health care. It carries minimal political risk. If patients pay for medicines privately, the NHS avoids the cost of consultations too.

Governments encourage self medication under the ruse of enhancing patient choice and convenience.

7.7 The NHS internal market

Labour did not abolish GP fund holding or the internal market. It only renamed them (Webster 2002). The *1997 NHS Primary Care Act* converted GP fund holding into '*locality commissioning*' through 'primary health care trusts' (PCTs). The PCT quango is empowered to buy services from NHS and private providers. PCTs are scheduled to control 90% of healthcare funds (Majeed and Malcolm 1999).

Although service contracts are expected to last longer than under GP fund-holding, PCTs can still move contracts from provider to provider, looking for the cheapest and not necessarily the best service, searching for the intangible '*value for money'* (Dixon et al 1998).

7.7.1 The ruse of commissioning services

The scope and freedom of PCTs is determined by external political forces. Political pressures to control costs, to demonstrate improvements in the quality of health services and in patient satisfaction will increase.

PCT personnel, particularly GPs, will be encouraged, even coerced, into influencing the development and delivery of health care rather than only minding their own professional practice (Dixon et al 1998).

Health management expertise is scarce

PCTs have taken a bigger role in managing resources for primary and secondary care. They are obliged to work with private health care providers in agreeing and managing, short and long term service contracts (DH 2000). How did they acquire the expertise so fast? What is the risk of failure?

High quality is rarely cheap

PCTs will be under scrutiny for the quality and cost of services they commission. The pressure for cheap, high quality service will be intense. Unfortunately high quality is rarely cheap. The bureaucracy of commissioning through the private finance initiative and consulting competing private providers (as mandated by the concordat), is unlikely to guarantee low cost and high quality.

PCTs will be blamed if drug budgets are inadequate

PCTs are responsible for restricting growth in drug costs and hospital budgets. They will be blamed if allocated funds are insufficient and rationing prescription drugs becomes a 'crisis.'

Implementing amalgamated, cash limited budgets means that decisions taken by individual clinicians and managers about the use of resources will impact on PCT finances. If the money runs out patients may not receive essential drugs. This could become a major political issue and could replace 'waiting list' and 'winter bed' crises.

Administration costs will increase

PCTs employ a full roster of management and administrative personnel to manage their unified budgets. PCTs are directed to establish integrated information systems that include utilisation and expenditure data for all practices and general practitioners. Running the NHS will be more expensive than it would have been if the internal market had not be created.

7.7.2 The facade of internal markets

The so called purchaser/provider split is a facade. PCTs are both purchaser and providers of health services. They buy services for their patients and also provide services to patients registered with individual GPs and practices. GPs spend most of their time on curative care and not on health promotion and preventive care as assumed by the DH.

The purchaser role was given to PCTs to reduce the influence of regional offices and health authorities, but mainly to clip the wings of hospital consultants.

7.7.3 Impact of strategic health authorities

Weaker strategic health authorities replaced regional offices and local health authorities. PCTs have a narrow locality focus and do not have the same impact on central government as former health authorities. Although not required to co-ordinate supra-PCT services, StHAs have no choice but to persuade PCTs and hospital trusts to work together.

Unless StHAs are effective in co-ordinating supra-PCT services, locality commissioning will be fragmented, inefficient and easier to starve of resources by DH bureaucrats.

It is self-evident that GP fund holding and its successor, locality commissioning, were created to control NHS expenditure and not to improve patient care.

7.7.4 The myth of health care markets

The *NHS and Community Care Act* split the service into purchasers and providers, but it did not create a true health care market (Baggott 1998). Locality commissioning and standard prices for surgical procedures are unlikely to create a true market. Even in the USA health care is an imperfect market. It does not obey the rules of supply and demand (Roberts 1998).

"Medicine is an imperfect market. In health care the purchaser is usually not the consumer, and the goods provided by the seller are difficult to define and often contingent on other aspects of care such as results of tests and treatments.

.... the medical marketplace does not follow the classic rules of supply and demand. Doctors ... set the demand of the care...can artificially increase demand...." (Roberts 1998).

Locality commissioning will not eradicate tensions between GPs and hospital consultants– it will make them worse. PCTs and hospitals will disagree over commissioned and delivered services, and over service priorities. Locality commissioning does not guarantee adequate funding for primary care and hospital care, nor does it guarantee 'value for money'– the highest quality of care at the lowest cost.

7.7.5 Purchasers may abuse their power

Providers depend on purchasers for survival. If a PCT shifts large contracts from a hospital trust, that hospital could fail. Would governments allow hospital trusts to fail?

The NHS is a social service and until health care is fully privatised governments will be forced by electoral considerations to maintain services or risk losing elections (Roberts, 1998). In the 2001 general election, Labour lost a 'safe' seat after down-grading a local hospital (BBC News, 8 June 2001).

7.7.6 Services must be 'bought' in advance

Because there is no guaranteed patronage, hospital trusts will not plan and develop new services on population based assumptions. Services must be commissioned before building, equipment purchase and staff recruitment can be considered. No hospital trust will have the resources and courage to develop and market a service.

An NHS hospital is not the same as a gadget factory that may be switched on and off according to demand for gadgets– it is not governable rules of supply and demand– by true market forces.

Few NHS hospitals would have the nerve to close Accident and Emergency departments because A & E services were losing them money. If a hospital had overspent its budgets and activity/cost analysis showed that the 'overspend' was causes by excess A & E activity– treating more people than budgeted for– that A& E was their most expensive (money losing) service, that hospital would not have the option, let alone the courage to act like a traditional business executive– close the division that was not only unprofitable, but lost a lot of money. The A & E (and NHS) is a social services and not a business profit centre.

7.7.7 Consequences of NHS internal markets

Primary care must be improved, but not by running down the hospital sector. Hospitals and primary care are mutually supportive; each must be able to fulfil its role for the whole NHS to meet its objectives– benefiting its clients (patients). Hospital waiting lists and winter bed crises are expected as small PFI built hospitals open. How will PCTs commission for winter pressures?

The NHS is a social system and works better when the social, medical and political implications of funding reforms are considered before the reforms are implementing (Heath 1997). A recent HOC Health Select Committee report on foundation hospitals, indicates that this is not happening (HOC Health Select Committee 2002-03). Hospitals trusts were invited and identified for foundation status *before* parliament had fully debated, let alone legislated for the establishment of foundation hospital trusts.

7.8 The private finance initiative

New Labour adopted two Conservative beliefs about public services– *that the private sector can deliver public services just as well as the public sector; and that nobody owes a living to public sector organisations, for their own sakes* (Kemp, 1999).

These two views are held by Labour as truths– false truths that however, are immune to evidence to the contrary, as demonstrated by Labour's enduring faith in the *private finance initiative*.

7.8.1 What is a private finance initiative?

Some public services have always been designed and built by private firms for the public sector. The Private Finance Initiative (PFI) was launched in 1992 by Norman Lamont, when he was Chancellor of the Exchequer in a Conservative government.

PFI is supposed to mobilise private money to finance services traditionally funded from the public treasury. PFI is supposed to *design, finance, build and operate services more cheaply than the public sector.* PFI projects are usually managed by a consortium (a construction company, a financier, a facilities management contractor and consultants).

Government claims that PFI *transfers the financial risk* of building and operating services from the public to the private sector and provides skills and innovative expertise apparently lacking in the public sector (National Audit Office 1998).

7.8.2 What is investment risk?

Investment risk is the likelihood of losing the investment. In the investment industry, government bonds and guaranteed investments carry less risk than private company bonds.

"***A bond** is essentially a loan. Bondholders lend money to governments or companies and are promised a certain rate of interest in return....UK government bonds....carry no risk..."* (Berger, Gardner and Gardner 2000).

"**Risk free rate of return**: *The yield on a risk-less investment. The relevant three-month government security is generally considered to be risk free"* (Morton, 1995).

While governments can use public taxes to redeem their bonds, if a company becomes bankrupt its bonds become worthless. Of course if the company is a big bank it is usually rescued by the central bank using tax payers' money. But that privilege does not extend to small business enterprises, like those that form PFI consortia.

PFI is now the preferred method of financing public services. Box 7.7 shows the range of projects funded through PFI.

7.7: Facilities built or managed under PFI	
Air traffic control	Prisons
Building refurbishment	Radio communications
Electronic re-engineering	Railways
Global telecoms	Roads
Hospitals, GP surgeries, clinics	Schools, colleges, universities
IS/IT infrastructure	Staff accommodation
Magistrates courts	Student accommodation
Office accommodation	Underground transport systems
Police stations	Waste management
Power and Energy	Water and sewage systems

Owen and Merna, 1999

7.8.3 Need for PFI not credible on financial grounds

After studying many NHS PFI projects, Pollock and others have shown that PFI funded projects cost more than they would if financed directly by the Treasury. While governments can borrow at 3.0% to 4%, PFI consortia charge between 9.1% and 18.5 % of construction costs (Pollock et al 1999, Gaffney et al 1999) as shown in Box 7.10.

In the financial appraisal of Carlisle Hospital, it was only after interest rates of 6% or more were used that PFI looked better (Gaffney et al 1999). At 5.5 % or less, the analysis favoured public funding.

At a 4% interest rate, Carlisle Hospital managers could have spent £231.9m on building a hospital. At 6% they could only afford £174.34m to build a smaller unit. How were managers at Carlisle Hospital persuaded to accept an inferior funding option? Why?

7.8.4 PFI invades the public sector

A government Private Finance Panel has identified extra public sector functions it believes are suitable for PFI (Box 7.8).

Box 7.8: Extra public functions identified for by Private Finance panel for future PFI	
Agriculture	Chancellor's department
Defence	National heritage
Education	Overseas development agency
Employment	Scotland
Environment	Social Security
Home office	Trade sand industry
Legal department	Transport
Northern Ireland	Wales

Owen and Merna, 1999

The Treasury directive that NHS trusts discount their capital costs at 6% per year when comparing PFI funding with public funding disguises the extra cost of PFI. In 1999, a National Audit Office's report on Dartford and Gravesham Hospital PFI project found that potential benefits of PFI were exaggerated by millions (National Audit Office, 1999). Why?

7.8.5 PFI shrinks hospital capacity

The NHS acute sector is shrinking under PFI. The capacity to care for patients is being deliberately reduced. When its PFI project is completed, South Manchester Hospitals Trust will have lost 48.9% of its former capacity (Box 7.9).

Most PFI projects are designed for a high all year bed occupancy– like hotels. There is no flexibility (reserve capacity) for peak periods of activity– winter peaks in admissions, accidents disasters (Economist 1995). Unlike hotels, hospital A& E departments are not free to hang "No Vacancies" sign outside the main entrance when their beds are full. So trolleys are used and eventually constitute 'political crises'.

Box 7.9: Reduction in NHS beds under PFI developments

Hospital trust	1995-6	1996-7	Planned	Change 96-7 (%)
Bromley Hospitals	610	625	507	-18.90
Calderdale Healthcare	797	772	553	- 28.40
Dartford and Gravesham	525	506	400	- 20.95
North Durham Acute	665	597	454	- 23.95
Norfolk and Norwich	1120	1008	809	- 19.74
South Manchester	1342	1238	736	- 48.95
Worcester Royal	697	699	390	- 44.20
South Buckinghamshire	745	742	535	- 27.89
Hareford Hospitals	397	384	250	- 34.89
Carlisle	506	507	465	- 8.28
Greenwich	660	566	484	- 14.49
Total	**8083**	**7634**	**5583**	**- 26.87**

Pollock, Dunningan, et al, 1999.

7.8.6 PFI costs more for less

Ironically, PFI increases unit costs. Completed PFI projects have higher operational costs. Bromley Hospitals Trust's PFI payments are expected to consume 14.7% of its income compared with 11.4% before the PFI funding project. The project reduced the trust's acute capacity by 20% (Pollock and Gaffney 1998).

7.8.7 PFI transfers public property to private financiers

PFI is accused of being a conduit for transferring public property to private financiers (Economist 1995, Robinson 2000). This privatisation of public property (Box 7.10) and the concomitant 20 - 50 year mortgages, payable by future taxation, is called *'transfer of financial risk'* by Tory and Labour politicians. Who is spared the financial risk?

Box 7.10: Costs and annual rent of PFI built hospitals (£m)

Trust	Income 1996-7	assets 1996-7	PFI build (£m)	1996-7 capital costs*	PFI rent (£m)	Rent/ income (%)	Rent/ Cost
Calderdale	72.2	35.2	64.6	4.7	9.0	12.4	13.1%
Carlisle	46.3	19.6	64.7	2.7	8.0	17.3	12.4%
Greenwich	95.2	55.0	84.0	8.7	11.0	11.5	13.1%
Norfolk/Norwich	122.1	19.0	143.5	12.7	15.6	12.8	15.5%
North Durham	59.0	24.9	61.0	3.6	7.1	12.0	11.6%
Wellhouse	83.6	105.0	54.0	5.2	10.0	12.0	18.5%

After Gaffney, Pollock, et al. 1999

** Interest, depreciation and rental.*

7.8.8 Is PFI creative accounting?

Government critics claim that PFI artificially inflates the amount of money available for tax cuts and limiting tax increases. PFI enables governments to provide electorally desirable services– schools, hospitals, roads– without paying for them at the time.

Commitment to pay rent for PFI projects does not appear in current public sector borrowings. If the projects were funded by the Treasury, its accounts would show the extent of public borrowing. Therefore PFI enables government to borrow and spend without increasing (declared) public debt (Kemp 1999). *That is creative accounting.*

To ensure that the public is not provoked into electoral revolt by drastic changes in welfare provision, major fiscal and social policy changes are introduced and implemented stealthy. The merits of PFI and the concordat with private medicine were hardly debated in parliament. Calls from MPs for piloting PFI were ignored by Conservative and Labour governments.

7.8.9 Should citizen fret about PFI?

The public should examine the justification and morality of PFI:

- PFI creates a feeling that the Treasury is keeping essential financial information off the balance sheet. PFI commitments do not appear in current public spending (Kemp,1999)

- PFI looks like public finance mismanagement when government orders public institutions undertake long term financial contracts whose economic consequences have not been evaluated

- government is committing future tax payers to 25 to 50 years of mortgage payments. The social, economical or technical need or value of most the PFI projects will have expired well before the mortgage is repaid

PFI is used to finance and operate public services that democratic governments will not allow to fail unless they wish to commit electoral suicide. PFI projects serve people whose votes count at general elections.

- If government can borrow at 3 - 4% interest, why is it anxious to mortgage public services at 18%? Why is government exposing public organisations to financial risk– failure to pay the mortgage?

- If a PFI consortium fails who will rescue its commitments?

- Is PFI a political instrument– that keeps public sector borrowing from scrutiny– enabling elections to be won?

- Is PFI a tool for transferring services to the private sector?

7.9 Foundation hospital trusts

NHS Foundation Trusts are "public sector corporations" with members instead of shareholders. The *Health and Social Care (Community Health and Standards) Bill* is intended to establish foundation hospitals that are:

- independent legal entities, free to determine their relationship with patients, staff, the local community and other stakeholders, free of line management from the DH

- part of the NHS and will provide healthcare to NHS patients within national standards

- accountable to the local community through '*payment for results*' or '*cash for performance*' contracts based on regulated price tariffs

- inspected by the Commission for Health Audit and Improvement (CHAI) to national standards in the same way as other NHS and independent healthcare providers

- empowered to embark of future PFI projects, recruit and employ staff, pay them flexibly and offer additional rewards

- expected to contribute to the education and training of health professionals, and workforce development (DH July 2002)

7.9.1 Unison opposes foundation hospitals

Unison, the largest UK trade union, with 1.3 members (2003) many of whom are NHS employees, strongly opposes the establishment of foundation hospital trusts. It has published 7 reasons for its position (Unison 2003). Briefly, foundation hospitals will:

- *compete as part of a commercial market*– under competitive PCT commissioning relatively small changes in demand could destabilise small hospitals and lead to their closure

- *be backdoor to privatisation*– private sector providers would be eligible to become foundation trusts

- *not lead to greater local accountability or social ownership*– foundation hospitals would not benefit the whole public but only a their 'members'

- *be poor value for money*– by borrowing private capital for developments, foundation hospitals would incur higher costs than if they had borrowed through the public sector. They would also be more expensive to run (contracting and managing *'payment for results'*)

- *lead to greater inequalities between hospitals*– foundation hospitals would have better access to capital finance and could borrow at the expense of non-foundation hospitals if the borrowings came from DH spending limits

- *draw scarce staff away from non-foundation trusts*– by paying better salaries, foundation hospitals would steal staff from non-foundation trusts. Staff would be drawn to foundation hospital by better reputation

- *undermine the NHS public service principle*– health planning would become disjointed, equality and equity would be lost, sharing of best practices would cease under market competition.

Frank Dobson, Labour health secretary, 1997-1999, has highlighted *'Labour's unhealthy addiction to change'* (Dobson 2003) and strongly opposed the establishment of foundation hospitals.

7.9.2 Labour think-tank wants foundation hospitals

The Health Policy Consensus Group (2003), a think-tank of the Institute for the Study of Civil Society, has published a report *'A New Consensus for NHS reform,'* on future funding and governance of the NHS. The group includes senior Labour supporters, academics, and a hospital consultant. The report supports the creation of foundation hospitals and recommends that:

- state hospitals should become independent foundation hospitals as soon a possible with their assets forever used for health care. NHS hospitals should not be transferred to private commercial ownership

- PCTs should be changed into American style health maintenance organisations (just independent or privatised?)

- individuals must buy (compulsory) health insurance from a range of insurers; and financial resources should follow patient preferences

- government should create legal and regulatory frameworks to ensure that patients get high quality health services

- government must ensure that accident and emergency services and essential public health services are available

- government must ensure that if a hospital gets into financial difficulty appropriate action will be taken

- foundation hospitals should be free to borrow money in capital markets; such loans should not count towards government public borrowing

- patients should have a choice of competing healthcare providers and politicians must not override the professional duty of clinicians to act in the patient's interest.

The report is partly contradictory. Why should government, in the event of *"a hospital being in financial difficulty take appropriate action,"* to save an independent business? Why does Labour need pseudo-autonomous foundations?

7.9.3 ONS reveals limit foundation hospitals' powers

The Office of National Statistics (ONS) classifies foundation hospitals as "public benefit corporation" (ONS July 2003).

"Foundation Trust will have additional freedoms, compared with existing NHS Trusts, but their ability to determine their corporate policy will be restricted by government involvement through restriction in both the planned legislation and regulatory powers:

- *The imposition of borrowing limits*
- *A legal duty to follow NHS values*
- *Regulatory approval needed to amend constitutions."*

7.9.4 Foundation hospitals at large

The 1997 NHS Primary Care Act abolished local health authorities and regional offices and replaced them with weaker strategic health authorities (StHA). Apparently StHA will have no statutory power over foundation hospitals.

Foundation hospitals will be governed by their own boards drawn mainly from the private sector. According to the *'Health and Social Care (Community Health and Standards) Bill'* which is before parliament, local control will be minimal, although Labour spin makes it sound as if enhancing local control was the impetus for creating foundation hospitals.

Deliberate chaos

Is this planned chaos? How will the needs of the wider population be coordinated? Are these structures designed for a time when health care will be fully privatised and coordinated by markets forces?

Foundation hospital boards direct patient advocacy

Apparently patient advocacy in foundation hospitals *will not* be provided by PALS, PPIF, ICAS or OSC statutory bodies that the rest of the NHS is obliged to deal with, but by their hospital boards. Government abolished community health councils, it claimed, because the single body could not, without conflict:

- to monitor the operation of local health services,
- to give advice to health authorities, and
- to be consulted about substantial changes in services.

Apparently foundation hospital boards will not experience the alleged conflict of roles. Is it because the majority on the board will represent private business that the there will be no conflict in roles. Will foundation hospital boards have skills and wisdom denied to CHCs?

Patient advocacy would limit business 'freedoms'

Foundation hospitals are designed to usher the NHS into healthcare markets. Statutory patient advocacy would hamper the trust's business freedoms. Foundation hospital trust boards need not waste time over such issues as accountability, equity and 'value for money' that would interest local residents and borough councils.

7.10 Labour breaks promise to the elderly

About 20% of people in England are over 60 years of age. In 2003, the cost of caring for an old person in a residential home was about £260 to £450 per week; nursing home care cost £350 to £800 per week (www.capitalcare.co.uk).

Tory politicians cite the increasing number of elderly people as the reason for reducing welfare services. They have used phrases like *personal choice, reducing government, private provision,* and *increasing choice.* Such phrases suggest that *"because there will be more elderly people in the future, we must set up mechanisms for them to starve or die of cold without society holding us responsible for their suffering"* (Watson 2000).

7.10.1 Let markets solve social issues!

When Conservatives regained power in 1979, their agenda for social policy was: *to remove social decisions from the elected government, and to make them by-products of the pursuit of profit in deregulated markets* (Hart 1994).

On 27th July 2000, prime minister, Tony Blair, presented *'The NHS Plan: a plan for investment, a plan for reform'* to parliament. Under the plan, government declined to fund personal care for residents of nursing homes. The plan did not refer to services as *'free at the point of delivery'* either.

"From October 2001, subject to a decision by Parliament, nursing care provided in nursing homes will be fully funded by the NHS" (DH 2000).

7.10.2 Government broke a 52 year old promise

Most elderly people were promised *care from the cradle to the grave* when they paid national health insurance contributions. That promise has been broken. If government were an insurance company it would be sued for breach of contract. Equitable Life was successfully sued when it attempted to renege on guaranteed annuity payments. Unfortunately for the elderly, governments have the power to make and change rules (law).

"The Court of Appeal ruled that Equitable....had been wrong to pay policy- holders radically different final bonuses.....Equitable was in breach of its contractual agreements ... had engaged in an "impermissible exercise of discretion..." (Lumsden 2000).

7.10.3 Closure and sale of nursing homes

The private nursing homes industry has come under financial pressure. In October 1999 Advantage Healthcare, a nursing home operator went bankrupt (Times 1999a). Soon after that, BUPA withdrew a £250m bond issue from the investment market because of lack of investor interest (Times 1999b).

Chronically under-funded social service departments had failed to pay adequately for their sponsored residents. Private nursing homes continue to go out of business (Times 1999a).

"Thousands of elderly people in need of residential care are finding it harder to find places as 18 residential homes a week close across Britain. ... more than 15,000 beds were lost last year, at a time when the population of people over 75 is rising faster than ever.

The crisis is acute in the most affluent areas, where booming property prices put pressure on care home owners to sell up. Most homes closed over the past year are being converted to residential occupation" (Summerskill 2001).

Private health care providers know the financial risk associated with government generated business. That is why they did not expanded private surgical capacity despite long NHS waiting lists for elective surgery. Instead they persuaded the DH to build DTCs, even in private hospitals, and offered to run them (DH 2002).

As nursing homes close, hospital bed-blocking gets worse (BBC News, 10 Nov 1999). Government reforms have accelerated nursing home closures. Frank Ursell, CEO, Registered Nursing Home Association recently wrote:

"We have been telling the Government time and time again that too many homes are on the edge of going out of business. But they behave as though everything is the garden is fine. They really need a reality check somewhere along the line."

"The government's policies in this area are disjointed to say the least. On the one hand they introduce new standards that we are expected to meet. On the other hand, they make it virtually impossible for us to find the necessary resources. It looks as though the Government has lost control of the situation" (Ursell 2003)

7.11 Concordat with private medicine

On 31st October 2000, a Labour government signed an agreement with the Independent Healthcare Association setting out the terms of a partnership between the NHS and private medicine. The *'Concordat with the Private and Voluntary Health Care Provider Sector'* states:

"...there should be no organisational or ideological barriers to the

delivery of high quality healthcare free at the point of delivery to those who need it, when they need it."

Under the concordat, the NHS will agree contracts for its patients to be treated in the private sector at the taxpayers cost (DH 2000).

A number of Labour MPs were upset that a Labour government signed a concordat with the private health industry. David Hinchliffe, Labour MP and chairman of the Commons Health Select Committee, was quoted in *The Independent:*

"It is very wrong of the Government to get into bed with the private sector which has, over 50 years of the NHS, constantly attempted to undermine the concept of state health care. To me, giving comfort at a time when it is known that the private sector is struggling is not something that I would expect a Labour government to do" (Grice, 2000).

Government ministers denied that their concordat would lead to privatisation of the NHS by the backdoor.

7.11.1 A marriage of political expediency

The NHS was made to embrace private medicine and health care markets through the 'concordat'. The concordat focuses on three areas of joint working:

- elective care (mainly elective surgery)
- critical care (intensive care), and
- intermediate care (nursing homes).

Details of service delivery are left to be made according to local availability of private providers. It also dictates a close working relationship with local private health care providers. These relationships may, where appropriate, be formalised in service agreements for long term healthcare provision, the concordat affirms.

What is expected of the NHS

The concordat with private medicine states that:

- treatment by private health care providers is cheaper and services quality is higher than in the NHS

- the association with private providers will ensure a wider range of health facilities locally

- private health care providers should be involved in the planning of local health services

- health authorities should ensure that local private health care providers are involved in the development of local health improvement programmes as appropriate

- the commissioning agency must ensure that appropriate standards and guidelines are followed; the private provider must achieve the standards.

The concordat calls for locally agreed protocols for patient referral, admission and discharge from NHS and private health facilities. It also urges the NHS to agree social care plans, discharge arrangements and joint information systems with social service departments and private providers.

The concordat states that in order to support an effective partnership, the NHS and private employers should identify existing and future local staffing needs. Information on the supply and demand of professionals in the private and public sectors should be shared, purportedly to support planning and training of health professionals, to develop human resources and for managing adverse clinical events.

What the private sector promises

Under the concordat the private sector is expected to:

- provide spare hospital capacity for NHS patient care
- provide people and management skills to run failing trusts
- form joint healthcare business ventures with NHS trusts
- recruit and provide overseas clinicians for NHS hospitals
- provide intermediate care in nursing home and community.

Local commissioners must demonstrate that they have involved private health care providers in planning processes and have made clear and open decisions on NHS service development. International firms may be involved in financing, building, and operating NHS services. Should the public be concerned about another Enron?

7.11.2 Implications of the concordat

The concordat can be seen as a means of forcing the NHS to transfer (and pay for) patient care in the private sector. If the NHS is not adequately funded it will not have the resources to negotiate and supervise such contracts.

The impetus for outsourcing health care is political and not patient interest. It is not based on *'lack of expertise'*, *'economies of scale' or 'focusing resources'* (Cordon, Wollmann and Heikkila 1999).

Transferring health care to the private sector is aided by the reductions in NHS hospital capacity through PFI (Pollock et al 1999). The transfer of NHS patients to the private sector infuses new life into a industry that was struggling for survival (Hinchcliffe 2000).

Diverting resources to the private sector

If payments to private providers come from existing budgets, scarce resources will be diverted from the NHS to the private sector. Although the concordat is less radical than the 1987 Tory NHS privatisation agenda, the distinction between Labour and Tories on health care has become blurred.

The private sector rarely trains its own staff, but poaches experienced staff from the NHS. It only runs brief lucrative postgraduate seminars and not the long and costly professional courses.

NHS professionals to follow patients into private sector

By requiring NHS staff to follow NHS patients into the private sector, the concordat makes it easier for the private sector to identify and poach the best NHS staff (Hinchcliffe 2000).

Professionals who disliked profiting from patient suffering usually dedicated their careers to working in the NHS. If*, "there should be no ideological barriers'* to treating NHS patients in private health facilities, then there will be *'no moral consideration'* to keep these health professionals in the NHS.

Private medicine cherry-picks NHS services

By requiring health authorities to involve private providers in the planning and development of local services, the concordat permits the private sector to cherry-pick profitable elements. The concordat does not require the private sector to consult the NHS before developing its health care business.

The cherry-picking is done by government, when NHS staff and property– Diagnosis and Treatment Centres, are handed to the private sector to manage for a profit (DH 2002).

7.12 Diagnosis and Treatment Centres

Under the Conservatives, NHS hospitals were managed as hotels. Hospital beds and wards were closed to achieve high bed occupancy rates– a key efficiency measure. To become *'efficient'* the NHS closed hospitals wards and small hospitals. Nurses and support staff lost jobs. Labour contributed to the "efficiency drive" by commissioning smaller hospitals through PFI schemes.

7.12.1 NHS beds closed to create 'need for capacity'

Conservative governments eliminated 'excess' capacity (wards and hospitals) to improve service efficiency. New Labour used PFI to replace old big hospitals with smaller units. South Manchester University Hospitals NHS Trust lost 48.95% of its capacity through PFI (Pollock, Dunningan et al 1999).

Because of *accounting efficiency*, and not patient needs, hospitals lost capacity and flexibility for winter pressures. As predicted, and communicated to government by NHS staff and the BMA, winter pressures led to cancellation of elective surgery. Surgeons and theatres lay idle because surgical beds were used for emergencies. Surgical waiting lists grew longer.

The press published 'scandals' of patients sleeping on trolleys in A&E. Questions were asked in parliament about trolley waits, cancelled operations and longer waiting lists. The case for *growing (surgical) capacity* was made.

Of course waiting is not limited to surgery– that would be unfair! Sexual health clinics, cardiac investigations, childhood mental health and many non-surgical services have long waits too. However few politicians are keen to table parliamentary questions on sexual health.

7.12.2 Re-open beds for the private sector

Government had to re-create capacity (replace what Tories and Labour deliberately shed). However, the 'new' capacity is isolated form the *NHS*, given to private sector firms to manage, or built in the private sector (*Growing capacity*, DH 2002).

Why did the private health sector refrain from expanding its business– creating surgical capacity– despite shortage of NHS surgical beds? The private sector had learnt its lesson. During the Conservative era, private nursing homes were built only to be closed and converted into residential accommodation, when they could not make a profit on local authority sponsored residents (Ursel 2003).

Under *Growing Capacity,* the NHS builds surgical units in NHS or private hospitals (DH 2002). Even when located in NHS hospitals with NHS staff, DTCs are managed by private firms. Support services, like laboratory and radiology, are contracted from the host hospital.

DTCs are publicised as expanding '*patient choice'* (DH 2002). Was the concordat responsible for *growing capacity* for the private sector?

The big political debate is currently over foundation hospitals. But the study concludes that it is the introduction of choice, and a bigger mix of public and private providers, that will have "profound consequences for the management of health services in England" (Timmins 2003)

Better "patient choice" increases the likelihood of Labour winning a third term in office; but 'choice' has its unpredictable effects:

It may also "fuel demand for services of questionable effectiveness", the study found and it warned ministers that limits would have to be set or financial control would be lost. "No healthcare system in the world offers complete freedom of choice. There will be limits to choice and these need to be explicit and understood" (Timmins 2003).

7.12.3. Concentrate of profitable cures (surgery)

Mental health, learning disability, pre-surgical coronary heart disease and sexual transmitted diseases are difficult to classify into health resource groups (HRG) and finished consultation episodes (FCE). Therefore they are not itemised in '*Reforming NHS Financial Flows-Payment by Results*' (DH 2002). So what? So they do not receive targeted budgets or dedicated treatment centres. DTCs are dedicated to profitable surgical procedures (Box 7.11)

It is no accident that not much attention, or money, has been dedicated to increasing access for learning disability, sexual health and other non-surgical conditions. Sorry– they are not profitable.

Box 7.11: Work at Diagnosis and Treatment Centre = surgery!	
Ophthalmology (cataracts) Cardiac revascularisation Ear, nose and throat Orthopaedics and trauma Gastroenterological (intestinal)	Diagnostic endoscopy Urological Gynaecological Breast surgery Vascular surgery, etc.

Money will follow the patient. That has led hospitals to start direct marketing to patients - advertising either their waits or innovative ways of treatment in order to attract business

*NHS hospitals are likely to start advertising for business as the health service gives patients the right to choose which hospital to go to for routine surgery...(*Timmins 2003).

Unprofitable conditions neglected

A recent Commons Health Select Committee report on Sexual Health revealed the explosion in sexually transmitted diseases. It found that services for sexual health were very inadequate– incapable of stemming the tide of chlamydia, gonorrhoea, syphilis, HIV and other conditions (Hawkes 2003).

Where is preventive care?

Prevention, early diagnosis and treatment can and do reduce the need for surgery in future by preventing complications that may require surgery. Examples of such conditions are shown in Box 7.12 below.

Box 7.12: Examples of when prevention/early treatment may reduce future need for surgery	
Condition	**Future need for surgery**
Chlamydia infections	Blocked Fallopian tubes (infertility)
Gonorrhoea in women	Blocked Fallopian tubes (infertility)
Gonorrhoea in men	Urethral strictures (blocked urethra)
Diabetes, type 2	Arterial/ ischaemic heart disease
Smoking	Heart attacks and revascularisation
Obesity	Ischeamic heart disease
Viral genital infections	Cancer of the cervix, penis
etc	**etc**

Unfortunately, politicians' futures are measured in 4 - 5 year bits– a government's term in office. Politicians prefer activities that produce quick results to point out and remind the public of he benefits the politician and party has brought them. So it is with diagnosis and treatment centres and foundation hospital trusts.

7.12.5 Why isolate the DCT from the NHS hospital?

DTCs are identifiable, have a powerful name and high profile. They are eminently useful during electioneering when they are identified as examples of *"improved patient choice."* DTCs are visible, countable (measurable) and reproducible (can build more or re-open and rename closed hospital wards).

Are DTCs electioneering tools? Definitely– otherwise why bother with concordats (to send old Labour to sleep), PFI (avoid need for high taxes, now) or the *National Insurance Contributions Act 2002* ('grow' a cash cow *before* old Labour stirs)?

8. Labour Implements Tory Agenda

The seven point 1987 Conservative agenda to transform the NHS has been closely followed by Labour. How far has Labour, accidentally advanced the Tory agenda for privatising the NHS? How well has Labour advanced Tory policy– *to remove social decisions from the elected government, and to make them by-products of the pursuit of profit in deregulated markets*?

8.1 Establish the NHS as an independent business

- current (2003) NHS reforms have handed the control of general practice to consortia of GP practices– primary care trusts (PCTs). PCTs are modelled on American (private) Health Maintenance Organisations; many PCTs are ripe for privatisation

- hospital trusts are tied to PCTs by locality commissioning– a financing arrangement designed to facilitate commercialism in privatised PCTs and foundation hospitals

- a bill to create autonomous foundation hospital trusts is before parliament. Labour has the majority to make it law, to create commercial health care quangos financed through the *National Insurance Contributions Act 2002.*

8.2 Integrate the NHS into private medical care

- the 'Concordat' with private health care providers discarded moral arguments for keeping private medicine out of the NHS– *"there should be no organisational or ideological barriers to the delivery of high quality healthcare..."*

- the 'Concordat' has enabled Diagnosis Treatment Centres (DTCs) to integrate private health services into NHS service provision, often in the same hospital

- *'NHS Financial Flows: payment by result'*, has made commercial transactions easier and enabled the NHS to out-sources patient care from the private sector and to expand UK health care markets.

8.3 Extend direct charging in a costed service

- charging for dentures, spectacles, appliances and prescribed drugs is well established. The precedent was established in 1951 when charging for dentures was introduced. Even the resignation of the founding minister of health, Aneurin Bevan (Webster 1991) did not prevent charging from becoming an established tool for rationing health care and collecting revenue

- As the cost of individual health care services and operations (products) are established by *NHS Financial Flows: payment by result,* clients (patients) will be charged the full cost of the product (consultation, prescription, operation, bed bath, grooming, talk, etc).

8.4 Devolve NHS responsibility to district level

[Devolve all responsibility for patients' care to directly funded district health authorities, dismantle regional health authorities and their

planning function, encourage individual hospitals to opt out and to compete for patients]

- health authorities and regional offices have been replaced by primary care trusts (PCTs) and advisory strategic health authorities (StHA). A bill to transform hospital trusts into foundation hospital trusts is before parliament (2003)

- PCTs are expected to eventually control 90% of funds for local health services– fragmented defused responsibility

- the concordat ensures that time and effort will be spent by StHAs, PCTs, hospital trusts, foundation hospitals, private providers, charities, the local community and other stakeholders consulting each other. Is such a diffusion of responsibility productive?

8.5 End national wage bargaining for NHS staff

- national wage bargaining for doctor and dentists, nurses and midwives and similar cadres survives, but just. Dissatisfaction nurses' pay has contributes to the shortage of native nurses in the NHS

- A contract negotiated between DH and BMA was rejects by constants and specialist registrars in England in 2002. NHS managerialism, mainly the NHS confederation, complicated negotiations. Milburn, then secretary of state for health vowed not to renegotiate the contract.

From Alan Milburn's concerted efforts to implement the rejected contract under local terms, the DH appears determined to end national pay bargaining. Markets prefer fragmented, non-unionised workforces. Ending national pay bargaining would improve the marketability of PCTs and foundation hospitals were they ever offered for sale.

In July 2003, the battle over national pay bargaining was postponed to another day. The DH and BMA may have found a temporary solution:

John Reid, the health secretary, made peace with NHS hospital consultants in England last night after their negotiators accepted his offer of a revised contract that will no longer oblige doctors to do non-emergency work during evenings or weekends.

The British Medical Association will recommend its members accept a deal that will preserve consultants' right to treat private patients if they have first offered four hours' overtime to the NHS (Carvel 2003).

8.6 Rename the NHS to create a new business entity

- GPs have been corralled into more financially viable, manageable and eminently marketable PCTs

- DH controlled hospital trusts are to become autonomous "*foundation hospitals trusts,*" new business entities with freedom to borrow private capital, reward staff flexibly and enter into commercial contracts with the private sector– do business.

- after privatisation, *'NHS'* will be removed from all literature on health care to "improving patient choice."

- Primary care trusts and foundation hospital trusts will be the *new business entity* desired by the 1987 Tory agenda. They will have the power to engage in *not-for-profit* business transactions. Like the BBC, they will be financed from compulsory user fees– national insurance contributions, as enacted by parliament in 2002.

8.7 Create a national health insurance scheme

A national health insurance scheme has been created through the *National Insurance Contributions Act 2002– "An Act to make provision for, and in connection with, increasing national insurance contributions and for applying the increases towards the cost of the national health service"* (www.hmso.gov.uk/acts)

In 2003 an extra 1% national insurance contribution charge was imposed on incomes as low as £4,615 a year (£88.75 per week).

"From 6 April 2003 an extra 1% national insurance contribution (NIC) will be imposed on all earnings above the first £4,615 a year. High earners, both employed and self-employed, will lose most because there is no upper limit for the additional charge" (www.ima-accountants.co.uk accessed July 2003)

The creation of a national health insurance scheme under the *National Insurance Contributions Act, 2002,* has been accepted as a justifiable means of raising money to fund the national health service. The press has been helpful by not calling it *"a tax on earnings = an income tax".*

While income tax is not charged on earning above £40,000), the social insurance contributions charge starts at £4,615 a year and has not upper limit. Therefore an additional 1% on social insurance raises more revenue than 1% on income tax. No politician will complain if the press does not equate social insurance with income tax– it is a bonus.

The press appreciated that this was a step towards the creation of a compulsory health insurance system– something the conservative press has advocated for some time.

---

9. Saving the nation's health service

9.1 Prayer for a national health service

A government white paper (DH 2003) has proposed that DNA samples from all newborn babies should be kept for future genetic testing. Could the future be ruled by genetic testing (Connor 2003)? Could insurers use the information to deny medical insurance to those at risk of inherited risk of diseases? Could those afflicted by diabetes, hypertension, asthma, chronic bronchitis, arthritis and some cancers be denied medical insurance or charged prohibitive premiums?

Saving the NHS means ensuring that general taxation, the cheapest and fairest method of insuring against ill-health continues, or that if it has lapsed, is quickly restored.

If the NHS were privatised, could the suffering of the poor and uninsured majority reach such level that a major political party would be obliged to restore an accessible health service?

Could fear of losing office, or to gain office persuade a major political party to restore an equitable health insurance scheme via general taxation or compulsory social insurance? Any political party not persuaded by the suffering of the people to pull insurance against disease through compulsory social insurance or general taxation would risk being replaced.

The longer private medical insurance lasted as the standard method of covering the risk of disease, the lower the chance of reversing the system. Despite the shortcoming of the USA medical insurance system, President Clinton was unable to introduce a healthcare system accessible to all Americans– there were 45 million without medical insurance at the time (Hacker 1999). Entrenched capitalist interests and irreconcilable demands from competing factions ensured rejection of Clinton's plan.

After the NHS has been privatised, it will be difficult to re-establish an accessible publicly funded national health service.

Salvation for the NHS

A number of plausible developments in social and health care could individually or collectively lead to revival of a national health service. Salvation could arise from:

- rebirth of the Labour party (returning to its roots)
- failure of the concordat with private medicine
- failure of the medical insurance market
- emergence of a new political party.

Failure of the concordat and medical insurance markets would have to be serious enough to persuade the electorate to agitate for better access to health care. The threat of electoral revolt would have to be serious enough to convince a major political party to restore an equitable and accessible health service through a sharing of the cost of insurance against ill-health.

9.2 Can old Labour save the NHS?

If New Labour deserts its traditional support (the working, labouring classes) for the comforts of middle England– the middles classes, perhaps old Labour will remember its roots and represent its constituents before it is too late. Was old Labour:

- awake when PFI was used to fund public sector projects?
- attentive as PFI was used to shrink the national health service?
- sleepy when the concordat with private medicine was signed?
- aware that Labour broke a promise to the elderly when it denied personal care (a bath, grooming) to frail residents of nursing home?
- awake when the *National Insurance Contributions Act 2002* was passed to create a fund to facilitate health care markets?
- out of town when diagnosis and treatment centres were introduced to get private sector medical operatives into NHS hospitals?
- still socialist when its MPs abstained instead of voting against foundation hospital trusts?

There is some evidence that old Labour is waking up despite New Labour's mantra. Recently, old Labour has taken tentative steps to reclaim the Labour party (Maguire 2003). Is it too late?

In June 2003 old Labour stirred from its slumber. Its MPs could have caused the Labour government to lose a parliamentary vote on increasing university tuition fees. The government won by a mere 74 votes (Sky News). Had old Labour voted against the motion instead of abstaining, New Labour would have lost the vote. It was a sad day for democracy that old Labour did not have the courage to vote against New Labour. Such is the power of the party whip!

..... many backbenchers have strong ties with the unions and could defy the prime minister again if, as expected, the House of Lords

rejects the bill. Insiders at Unison and the GMB, which are threatening to cut constituency funding for Labour backbenchers who do not support their policies, said they would scrutinise how MPs voted (Adams 2003).

Old Labour has the power to save the NHS. It must remind New Labour that the welfare state is the price for ensuring support for the government. New Labour needs both the defectors from the Conservative party and old Labour support to win the next general election. Old Labour is getting firmer in its demand that the government reduces its reforming zeal.

On 8 July 2003, in a vote on foundation hospitals, government majority was further cut to a mere 35 votes:

... government majority cut from 164 to 35- its lowest since coming to power....62 Labour MPs, including two tellers, voting against the hospital plans.

"Despite all the arm twisting, the offers of concessions and warnings of electoral trouble ahead if they refused to back the government, most of the rebels refused to cave in" (BBC News).

9.3 Could the marriage with private medicine fail?

The concordat is enabling privatisation of profitable elements of the NHS. Following privatisation, health services could become inequitably distributed both geographically and in quality, with poorer areas sparsely served. For example, PFI projects have been approved and built faster in richer neighbourhoods than in economically deprived areas (Pollock, Dunningan et al 1999).

The concordat has inhibited rather than encouraged the development of additional capacity within the NHS. When new capacity (diagnosis and treatment centres) is created in an NHS hospital, it is handed over to a private company to manage (DH 2002). Could communities with small (PFI) hospitals, and constant bed crises exert their will through the ballot box?

9.4 Could private medical insurance fail?

After privatisation, or the creation of autonomous foundation hospitals, charging for services will be extended and higher charges imposed (market value) for services (products).

Those who could afford it would have to buy health insurance to cover the financial risk of unexpected illness or accident. The logic is simple– car drivers insure against car accidents, so will those who can afford it insure against sickness.

There will be a plethora of health insurers. Many will fail, and like failure of other forms of insurance, many clients will be left without protection (Financial Times, 23 June 2003).

Serious failure of the medical insurance market could occur if the majority of the population were unable or unwilling to buy medical insurance, and/ or denied insurance because of genetic risk of some disease.

9.4.1 Private medical insurers are failing

This is not fantastic speculation. Private medical insurance has become more expensive and restrictive. An increasing number of preexisting conditions are excluded from cover. For two years to 2000, BUPA, Britain's leading private medical provider, increased its premiums by 14%. PPP Healthcare, the second largest, raised its premiums by 12% in 1999 (Francis 2000).

Demand for health insurance is declining while the cost of claims is increasing, despite the fact that many people are said to be unhappy with the NHS. While 10% of the population had medical insurance in 1999, the number had declined to 6.3% in 2000. This disparity is causing huge losses among medical insurers– BUPA lost £20m in 1999 (Francis 2000).

9.4.2 Millions of Americans lack medical insurance

The number of USA residents without medical insurance increased from 30 million in 1987 to 45 million in 1998 (Josefson 2000 b) and 58 million in 2002 (Marwick 2002).

American elderly citizens increasingly find it difficult to obtain or retain suitable medical insurance. In 2001, 934 000 elderly and disabled Americans lost medical cover from their health maintenance organisations (Josefson 2000).

9.4.3 Majority may be denied medical insurance

Widespread use of cheap but accurate genetic tests could make it possible for insurers to routinely test applicants and deny insurance to those at high risk of developing inherited diseases (Charatan 2000). The numbers could be large if cheap and accurate tests for genetic risks of hypertension, diabetes mellitus, senile dementia, obesity and other conditions were available and are used routinely.

That people at risk of genetic disease are denied medical insurance is becoming a major problem in Europe. The republic of Ireland has created a fund for patients who cannot get medical insurance (Payne 2001).

9.4.4 Genetic testing could hurt insurers

Genetic testing could work against the insurer if a positive result is known to the policy buyer but not the potential insurer. Individuals at high risk of genetic disease could insure themselves while those at low risk might not. Insurers could go bankrupt if claims were higher than anticipated on basis of average population risk of disease.

"In economic theory, additional information is usually of benefit. But in the case of the impact of genetic testing on life assurance, both the industry and many of its potential customers could do better by living in ignorance" (Bakhshi 2001).

9.5 Would a major political party save the NHS?

The NHS will not be saved by Labour, the Conservatives, nor the Liberal Democrats. The Conservatives would love to privatise the service. New Labour is emulating and exceeding Conservative zeal for privatisation (Kemp 1999). The Liberal Democrats admire Labour's ideological transformation, as described in a former leader's biography (Ashdown 2000), and are unlikely to act differently if they won a general election.

Health care quangos like the National Institute for Clinical Excellence (NICE) and the Commission for Health Improvements (CHI) or its *successor*, the Commission for Health Improvement and Audit (CHAI), will not save the NHS either. They were created by government to support NHS reforms, standardise services and minimise electoral risk after stories of 'medical scandals' and 'postcode lottery' across the country. NICE has been accused of being a sophisticated tool of rationing health care (Smith 2000).

9. 6 Would a new party revive the welfare state?

If Labour, the Conservatives and the Liberal Democrats were unable or unwilling to save the welfare state, perhaps a new political force, a new political party, could arise and seize the opportunity– answer the people's need.

The Labour Party was formed to answer the cries of working (labouring) people because the Liberal Party had abandoned the *disadvantaged* classes of early 20th century Britain and become indistinguishable from the Tories.

"It is significant that the Labour Party was set up specifically to provide a voice for the working class. Although the Liberal government of 1906-11 had introduced reforms which were designed to ease the suffering of the disadvantaged, the Liberal Party could not claim to represent the working class in the way that the new Labour Party could" (Dobson et al. 1999).

The new party would not be based on labourers' suffering, but on well informed groups, united by lack of medical insurance, inability to get higher education for themselves or their children or inability to afford private housing.

The new party would not depend on industrial action (strikes, pickets and long marches (old Labour tactics), but on modern media (mobile phones and the internet) to co-ordinate their political activities. TV, radio and newspapers are too close to current power systems to help (initially).

Hopefully the new party would revive the sharing of insurance against ***ignorance*** (lack of education), ***squalor*** (pollution), ***idleness*** (unemployment), ***want*** (poverty) and ***"disease*** (lack of health care access) through a national welfare system financed from general taxation or compulsory social insurance.

Will this scenario "come to pass"? Small chance! however, it is unlikely that in 1900, the Liberal and the Conservative parties would have believed that labourers would enter parliament as MPs in 1906, govern the nation in 1924, let alone win a second term of office. Miracles do happen– with prayer and hard work.

References

1. Adams C. Unions line up to fight 'damaging' NHS change. *Financial Times*, 10 July 2003.

2. Appley J, Boyle S. Blair's billions: where will he find the money for the NHS? *BMJ* 2000; 320: 865-867.

3. Ashdown P. The Ashdown Diaries. Penguin Press, London 2000.

4. ABPI. Facts & Statistics from the Pharmaceutical Industry. Association of the British Pharmatheutical Industry, 2002. www.abpi.org.uk/statistics/section.asp?sect=1#2

5. Baggott R. Health and health care in Britain. Macmillan Press, London 1998.

7. Bakhshi V. When ignorance is the best policy. *Financial Times*, 13 January 2001.

8. Beattie J, Hardie A. Blair suffers rebellion over tuition fees. *The Scotsman,* 24 June 2003.

9. Beecham L. BMA leaders call for efficiency savings to be halted. *BMJ* 1996; 312:1497.

10. Benatar S. What makes a just healthcare system? *BMJ* 1996; 313: 1567-1568.

11. Berger D, Gardner D, Gardner T. The Motley Fool UK Investment Guide. Boxtree, London 2000.

12. Bevan G . Taking equity seriously: A dilemma for government from allocating resources to primary care groups. *BMJ* 1998; 316: 39-42.

13. Birch S. Increasing patient charges in the National health Services: a method of privatising primary care. *Journal of Social Policy* 1986; 15(2): 163-184.

14. Blenkinsopp A, Bradley C. Over the Counter Drugs: Patients, society, and the increase in self medication. *BMJ* 1996; 312: 629-632

15. Boseley S. Ten dirty hospitals get support to clean up. *The Guardian* 11 April 2001.

16. Bowling A. Health care rationing: the public's debate. *BMJ* 1996; 312: 670-674.

17. Bradley C, Blenkinsopp A. Over the Counter Drugs: The future for self medication. *BMJ* 1996; 312: 835-837.

18. BBC. Nursing home closures 'blocking hospital beds'. *BBC News,* Northern Ireland, 10 November 1999.

19. BBC. Trust me, I'm a doctor. *BBC News*. 8 June, 2001.

20. BBC. Older nurses an underused resource. BBC News 23 July 20030

21. BMA. Health Funding review. BMA report, February 2001.

22. Brown K. Europe reinvented: Transfer of state assets. *Financial Times*, 26 January 2001.

23. Cartwright F. A Social History of Medicine- Themes in British Social History. Longman, London, 1977

24. Challis L, Henwood M. Equity in the NHS: Equity in community care. *BMJ* 1994; 308: 1496-1499.

25. Carvel J. Consultants keep private work rights in NHS deal. *The Guardian,* 18 July 2003

26. Charatan F. Leading health maintenance organisation near bankruptcy. *BMJ* 2000; 320: 135.

27. Coast J. The rationing debate: Rationing within the NHS should be explicit: The case against. *BMJ* 1997; 314: 1118.

28. Connor S. Plan to store DNA of every baby to tailor health care. *The Independent June* 2003.

29. Cordon C, Wollmann TE, Heikkila J. Thinking about outsourcing. In 'Mastering Global Business'. FT Pitman London 1999.

30. Coxall B, Robins L. Contemporary British Politics, 2nd edition. Macmillan, London 1994.

31. Cranney M, Cranney J, Stubbs H. Limitation of over the counter sales of paracetamol. *BMJ* 1998; 317: 1657.

32. DH. The Government's Expenditure Plans 2000-2001, April 2000.

33. DH. The NHS Plan: a plan for investment, a plan for reform. HMSO London 2000.

34. DH. The NHS Plan: The Government's response to the Royal Commission on Long Term Care. HMSO London 2000.

35. DH. For the benefits of patients: A Concordat with the Private and Voluntary Health Care Provider Sector. HMSO London 2000.

36. DH. NHS Foundation Trusts: Eligibility Criteria and Timetable. July 2002. www.DH.gov.uk/nhsfoundationtrusts

37. DH. Growing Capacity: Independent sector diagnosis and treatment centres. 2002. www.DH.gov.uk/growingcapacity/

38. DH. Diagnosis and Treatment Centres– frequently asked questions. www.gov.uk/growingcapacity. Dec 2002

39. DH. Payment by results. HMSO London 2002 www.doh.gov.uk/nhsfinancialreforms

40. DH. Genetics White Paper: Our inheritance, our future- realizing the potential of genetics in the NHS. HMSO 2003

41. Dixon J, Harrison A. Funding the NHS: A little local difficulty? *BMJ* 1997;314:216

42. Dixon J, Holland P, May N. Primary care: core values Developing primary care: gate-keeping, commissioning, and *BMJ* 1998; 317: 125- 128.

43. Dobson A, Grant M, Roberts D. British politics in Focus. Causeway Press, Ormskirk 1999.

44. Dobson F. Defeat Labour's unhealthy addiction to change. *Financial Times,* 1 May 2003.

45. Dobson R. Welsh hospital recruits Filipino nurses. *BMJ* 1999; 318: 284.

46. Dobson R. Blood pressure controls needed to save on European health bills. *BMJ* 2002; 325:238; citing a study in *Blood Pressure* 2002;11:33-45).

47. Doyal L. The rationing debate: Rationing within the NHS should be explicit: The case for. *BMJ* 1997; 314: 1114- 1117.

48. The Economist. Private finance initiative. 9 September 1995.

49. The Economist. Prognosis: poor. 3 May 1997.

50. Emmerson C, Frayne C, Goodman A. Pressure in UK Health: Challenges for the NHS. Institute of Fiscal Studies. London 2000.

51. Financial Times. FSA ruling may reveal new holes in endowments. *Financial Times,* 23 June 2003

52. Foster G. 'Not nearly enough for the workload'. *Independent*, 19 December 2000

53. Francis C. BUPA to remedy declining customer base with heartbeat strategy. *Independent*, 8 October, 2000.

54. Frankel S, West R. Rationing And Rationality In The National Health Service: The Persistence Of Waiting Lists. Macmillan London 1993.

55. Frankel S, Ebrahim S, Smith GD. The limits to demand for health care. *BMJ* 2000; 321: 40-45.

56. Freemantle N, Bloor K. Lessons from international experience in controlling pharmaceutical expenditure. I: influencing patients. *BMJ* 1996; 312: 1469-1471.

57. Gaffney D, Pollock AM, Price D, Shaoul J. The private finance initiative: NHS capital expenditure and the private finance initiative- expansion or contraction? *BMJ* 199; 319: 48-51.

58. Gaffney D, Pollock AM, Price D, Shaoul J. The private finance initiative: PFI in the NHS- is there an economic case? *BMJ* 1999; 319: 116-119.

59. Grice A. Backbench anger at NHS deal with the private sector. *Independent,* 1 November 2000.

60. Grice A, Laurance J. Nurses' pay award 'will fail to ease long-term crisis' *Independent* 19 December 2000

61. Hacker JS. The Road to Nowhere: The Genesis of President Clinton's Plan for Health Security. Princeton University Press, Princeton 1999.

62 Hall J, De Abreu Lauenco R, Vincey R. Carrots and sticks– the fall and fall of private insurance in Australia. *Health Economics 1999; 8(8): 653-60.*

63. Hall S. Doctors welcome moderniser's end. *The Guardian* 13 June 2003

64. Ham C. Retracing the Oregon trail: the experience of rationing and the Oregon health plan. *BMJ* 1998; 316: 1965-1969

65. Ham C. Health Policy in Britain. Macmillan London 1999.

66. Harrison H, Dixon J, New B, Judge K. Funding the NHS- Can the NHS cope in future? *BMJ* 1997; 314: 139-42.

67. Hart JT. NHS reforms: A conspiracy exists. *BMJ* 1994; 303:739.

68. Hawkes N. Patients turned away to spread sexually transmitted diseases. *Timesonline* 11 June 2003.

69. Hazlewood P. Chief executive resigns after waiting list inquiry. *PA News,* 24 January 2001

70. Health Policy Consensus Group. A New Consensus for NHS Reform. CIVITAS 2003. http://www.civitas.org.uk/nhs/

71. Heath I. The creeping privatisation of NHS prescribing. *BMJ* 1994; 309:623-624.

72. Heath I. Threat to social justice. *BMJ* 1997; 314: 598.

723 Henley J. France serves up first class treatment- but at a price. *The Guardian,* 21 June 2000.

734 Hinchcliffe D, Hassell R. Should the NHS be in bed with the private sector? *Independent,* 5 November 2000.

75. Hoffman JR, Wilkes M. Direct to consumer advertising of prescription drugs. *BMJ* 1999; 318: 1301-1302.

76. HOC Health Select Committee. Foundation Trusts. Second Report of Session 2002-03. HMSO London 2003

77. HOC Health Select Committee. Sexual health. Third Report of Session 2002-03. HMSO London 2003

78. HOC Health Committee. Patient and Public Involvement in the NHS. 7th report 2002/03. HMSO London 2003

79. Hurt JT. NHS reforms: A conspiracy exists. *BMJ* 1994; 303:739.

80. Hutton W. New Life for Health: the Commission on the NHS. Vintage, London 2000.

81. Independent. 'Dirty' hospitals get three-month clean-up deadline. 9 January 2001

82. Josefson D. Almost a million elderly people seek new insurance cover. *BMJ* 2000; 321:322.

83. Josefson D. US doctors consider access to health care for all. *BMJ* 2000;321:1491

84. Kemp P. Please stop fiddling the books. *New Statesman.* 18th October 1999

85. Klein R, Dixon J. Cash bonanza for NHS. *BMJ* 2000; 320: 883-884

86. Laurence J. Pressure is on NHS this winter, says Blair. *Independent*, 5 December, 2000.

87. Laurence J. Investment of £87.5 million aims to cut deaths by cancer. *Independent*, 3 January 2001

88. Leathard A. Health Care Provision: Past, Present and future. Chapman & Hall, London 1990.

89. Lumsden G. Court of Appeal rules against Equitable Life. *The Times,* 22 January 2000

90. Maguire K. Left vows to reclaim Labour. *The Guardian*, 5 July 2003

91. Majeed A, Malcolm L. Unified budgets for primary care groups. *BMJ* 1999; 318: 772-776.

92. Marwick C. A total of 58 million Americans lack health insurance. *BMJ* 2002;325:678

93. Mathiason N. Labour gets into bed with private medicine. *Observer*, 19 November 2000.

94. Mill J S. Utilitarianism. In Mill JS, Bentham J, Ryan A. Utilitarianism and other essays. Penguin Books. London 1987

95. Mills RP, Heaton JM. Waiting list initiatives: crises management or targeting resources? *Journal of Royal Society of Medicine*, 1991; 84(7): 4405-407

96. Morton J. The Financial Times Global Guide to Investing: The secrets of the world's investment gurus. FT Pitman London 1995.

97. Murray M. Modernising the NHS: Patient care: access. *BMJ* 2000;320;1594-1596

98. National Audit Office. The Private Finance Initiative: the first four design, build, finance and operate road contracts. Press Notice 5/98. London 1998.

99. National Audit Office. The PFI contract for the new Dartford and Gravesham Hospital. Press Notice 39/99. London 1999.

100. New B. The rationing agenda in the NHS. *BMJ* 1996; 312: 1593-1601

101. New B. What business is the NHS in? Establishing the boundary of a health care system's responsibility. Institute of Public Policy Research, London 2000

102. Newdick C. Primary care groups and the right to prescribe. *BMJ* 1998; 317:1361-1365.

103. OECD. The French system, despite patient choice, is wasteful in the use of many of its resources. Over-prescription is common. *OECD Economic Survey 1999-2000.* Paris 2000.

114. Office of National Statistics. News release: ONS announces decision on Foundation Hospitals. ONS 2 July 2003

115. Owen G, Merna A. The Private Finance Initiative. Centre for esearch in management of projects. www.umist.ac.uk

116. Payne D. Ireland sets up fund for patients who cannot get insurance. *BMJ* 2001;322:128

117. Pollock AM, Gaffney D. Capital charges: a tax on the NHS. *BMJ* 1998; 317: 157-158.

118. Pollock AM, Dunningan MG, Price D, Shaoul J. The private finance initiative: Planning the "new" NHS: downsizing for the 21st century. *BMJ* 1999; 319: 179-184.

119. Pollock A. Will intermediate care be the undoing of the NHS? *BMJ* 2000; 321: 393-394.

120. Rogers A, Entwistle V, Pencheon D. Managing demand: A patient led NHS: managing demand at the interface between lay and primary care. *BMJ* 1998; 316: 1816-1819.

121. Prescription Pricing Authority. Drug Tariff. The Stationery Office, London. Dec. 2000.

122. Pyne R. Professional accountability and industrial action: contradictory or compatible. *British Journal of Nursing* 1995; 4(14): 833-836.

123. Ramsay D. Why nurse will keep on leaving the NHS. *Independent,* 17 December 2000.

124. Robbinson D. PFI A 30 Road: How Britain mortgaged the future. *Newstatesman*, 7 April, 2000.

125. Roberts J. Primary care: core values. Primary care in an imperfect market. *BMJ* 1998; 317:186- 189.

126. Rogers A, Entwistle V, Pencheon D. Managing demand: A patient led NHS: managing demand at the interface between lay and primary care. *BMJ* 1998; 316:1816- 1819.

127. Rosenthal MM. Whatever happened to the reform of American health policy? *BMJ* 1994; 309: 1383-1384.

128. RCN. RCN Briefing: Nurses Pay- Facts and Figures. website www.rcn.org.uk/press0012/164 visited Dec 2000

129. RCP. Allergy services totally inadequate. RCP News, 25 June 2003.

130. Ryan M., Birch S. Charges for health care: evidence on the utilisation of NHS prescribed drugs. *Social Science and Medicine* 1991; 33(6): 681-687.

131. Schaefer S. Milburn defends use of overseas nurses. *Independent,* 22 November 2000a.

132. Shaoul J. Charging for capital in the NHS trusts: to improve efficiency? *Management Accounting Research* 1998;9:95-112

133. BSkyB. Labour Suffers Tuition Revolt. *Sky News.* 24 June 2003

134. BSkyB. Allergy In The UK: NHS 'Can't Cope'. *Sky News.* 25 June 2003

135. Smith A. The Wealth of Nations. Penguin, London, 1982.

136. Smith R. The failings of NICE. *BMJ* 2000; 321:1363-1364.

137. Smith R. Take back your mink, take back your pearls. *BMJ* 2002; 325:1047-1048

138. Stocks, P. Changes to health targeting. *Social Policy Journal of New Zealand* 1993; 1: 60-73.

139. Summerskill B. Fear grips old as care home closures rise. *The Guardian,* 25 March 2001

140. Times. Receivers called in at nursing homes. *Times*, 21 October 1999 (a).

141. Times. Bupa drops bond. *Times*, 4 November 1999 (b).

142. Timmins N. The Five Giants: A biography of the welfare state. Fontana, London 1996.

143. Timmins N. Europe reinvented: Europe adopts UK approach to spreading the risk. *Financial Times*; January 26, 2001.

144. Timmins N. Health chiefs 'use trickery to attain performance targets'. *Financial Times,* 1 July 2003.

145. Timmins N. NHS hospitals to market services to patients. *Financial Times*, 14 July 2003.

146. Torrington D, Hall L. Human Resource management. Prentice Hall Europe, Hemel Hempstead 1998.

147. Unison. Seven reasons why UNISON is opposed to foundation Trusts. www.unisonoxonhealth.org.uk. March 2003.

148. Ursell F. More nursing home closures: Minimum wage increase likely to push many over the edge. Registered Nursing Homes Association News. www.rnha.co.uk/news. 2003

149. Wafer A. A marriage of convenience? *BMA News Review*, 16 December 2000.

150. Walley T. Prescription charges: change overdue? *BMJ* 1998; 317: 87-488.

151. Warden J. Efficiency savings here to stay. *BMJ* 1996;313:136

152. Watson R. NHS reforms 'will privatise care of elderly'. *The Times*, 11 August 2000.

153. Watson R, Manthorpe J, Andrews J. Nurses Over 50: Options, decisions and outcomes. Published for Joseph Rowntree Foundation by The Policy Press, 2003.

154. Webster C (editor). Aneurin Bevan on The National Health Service. OUP, Oxford 1991

155. Webster C. Local government and health care- the historical perspective. *BMJ* 1995; 310: 1584-1587.

156. Webster C. The National Health Service: A political History. OUP, Oxford 1998

157. Webster C. The National Health Service: A political History. OUP, Oxford 2002.

158. Whitehead M Equity issues in the NHS: Who cares about equity in the NHS? *BMJ* 1994; 308: 1284-1287.

159. Whitney R. National Health Crisis : A Modern Solution. Shepheard-Walwyn Ltd, London 1998.

160. Willman J. A Better State of health: a prescription for the NHS. Profile Books, London 1998.

161. Wise J. New variant CJD and BSE are linked. *BMJ* 1996; 313: 1100.

162. World Health Organisation. The World Health Organisation Report 2000. Health Systems: Improving Performance. WHO Geneva 2000.

Prelude to a Private NHS

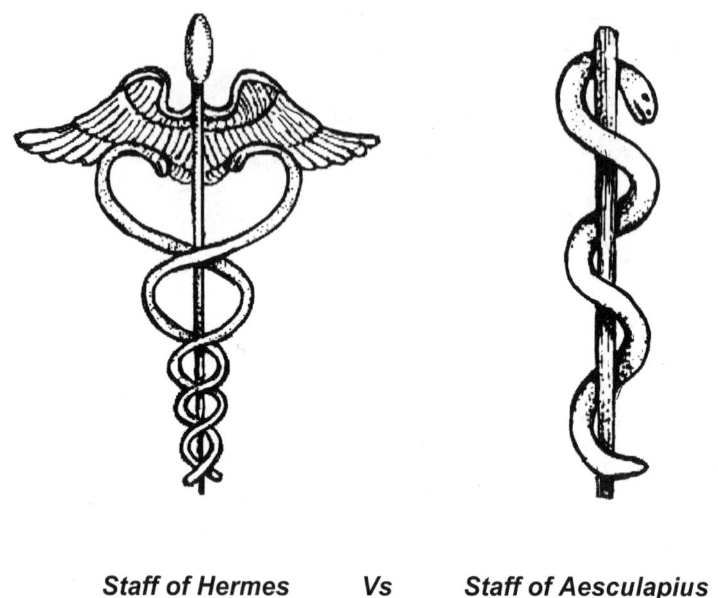

Staff of Hermes ***Vs*** ***Staff of Aesculapius***

Aesculapius, a Greek god of medicine, was famous for healing, wisdom and prudent action. His staff is the traditional symbol of healing arts.

Hermes was the god of wealth, commerce and thieves. His staff traditionally represented commerce. It is now a popular symbol for healing arts in USA.

http://www.in-ta.net/info/aesculapius/

Glossary

A & E = accident and emergency, hospital department receiving and treating accidents and emergencies

ABPI = Association of the British Pharmaceutical Industry

ACHC = Association of Community Health Councils

BBC = British Broadcasting Corporation (radio and TV)

BSB = British Sky Broadcasting (TV and radio)

BMA = British Medical Association; a quasi-trade union for doctors

BUPA = British United Provident Association

CEO = chief executive officer; administrative (management) head of an organisations

CHAI = Commission for Health Audit and Improvement; inspects NHS trusts, licenses and controls private healthcare providers

CPPIH = Commission for Patient and Public Involvement in Healthcare.

Concordat = an agreement between the DH and private medicine to collaborate in healthcare provision

DH = Department of Health, the ministry of health and social services

DTC = diagnosis and treatment centres; NHS built, privately managed surgical units,

Enron = a USA global trader in natural gas and electricity; collapsed from accounting fraud bankrupting employees and investors

FCE = finished consultation episode in health care; difficult to determine in chronic conditions.

GMB = General and Municipal and Boilermakers Union

GMC = General Medical Council; regulator of doctors in UK

GP = general medical practitioner; a general family doctor; first medical contact in British medicine

GDP = gross domestic product, a measures of the wealth created in a country each year

HRG = health resource groups; a grouping of medical/health conditions for costing/ tariff purposes

HOC = House of Commons

ICAS = Independent Complaints and Advocacy Services

MOH = medical officer of health

NAO = National Audit Office

NCAA = National Clinical Assessment Authority; a quango to assess the clinical skills of doctors reported to it

NICE = National Institute for Clinical Excellence; a quango to provide guidance on clinical standards and health care products

NHS = national health service

NMC = Nursing and Midwifery Council; regulator of nurses and midwives in UK

ONS = Office of National Statistics

Old Labour = traditional Labour supports; advocate social values

OECD = Organisation for Economic Co-Operation and Development

OSC = Overview and Scrutiny Committee; to provide local scrutiny of contested local NHS reorganisations

OTC = 0ver the counter– the pharmacy counter; over-the-counter; drugs you can buy without a doctor's prescriptions

PALS = Patient Advice and Liaison Service

PPIF = Patient and Public Involvement Forum

PMETB = Postgraduate Medical Education and Training Board

PCT = primary care trust, a corral of local GPs to create locality commissioning units

PFI = private finance initiative; Treasury system obliging the public sector to use private finance for public capital projects

PPP Healthcare = private patients plan healthcare; a medical insurance organisation.

RCN = Royal College of Nursing; nurses' trade union in uk

SHO = senior house officer

StHA = strategic health authority, a regional NHS quango to advise hospital trust and PCTs on managing health services

UNISON = Britain's biggest public sector employees' trade union; has 1.3 million members (2003).

WHO = World Health Organisation; an agency of the United Nations.

Acknowledgements

I would like to acknowledge the help and advice of the staff at The Library, the Education Centre, Trafford NHS Trust. Thank you.

I am indebted to Dr Janet Harvey, my supervisor for the MBA dissertation at Warwick Business School, for her guidance in the preparation of *'Prelude to a private national health service*'.

Thank to you kind friends and colleague for reading and critiquing *Prelude to a private NHS*.
